Tony Salerno's

Character Classics™

Teacher Activity Resource Book

Grades 3-4

CHARACTER BUILDING COMPANY™

Word to Teachers

The *Character Classics*™ series is designed to give students a basic foundation for character education through the use of contemporary lyrics set to classical melodies.

The *Character Classics*™ *Teacher Activity Resource Book* helps to reinforce the character qualities presented in the *Character Classics*™ musical recordings. The purpose of the activity books is to assist students in applying character qualities to their lives in everyday experiences. Students will also gain a knowledge of classical composers and some of the best and most loved melodies ever written.

The activities may be worked independently by some students, but you may also need to read and explain the instructions. This is also a good time to discuss the character quality that is being taught.

The *Character Classics*™ *Teacher Activity Resource Book* includes activities for character traits attentiveness, contentment, dependability, goodness, kindness, obedience, patience, perseverance, respect, self-control, thankfulness, and truthfulness. There is a Pledge to be signed upon completion of each unit. The lyrics to the songs are included in the activity book, along with some information about each composer. There is an answer key in the back for your convenience.

The Character Building Company hopes that this *Character Classics*™ series will encourage you in the knowledge that the best thing you could possibly do for your children is to instill positive principles in their lives. Students should know that character building values are not only something to learn about, but are values for the foundation of a successful life.

All songs in this series are adapted from the classics and may vary slightly from the original. To the best of our knowledge, our research is complete, but may not be the final word on the classics and their composers.

Contributors: Katherine Vawter, Edith Vawter, Patty Crowley, Donald Gunter, Shari Gunter, Jane Neidenfeuhr, and Scott Votaw
Illustrators: Tim Davis, John Blackford, Cesar DeCastro
Graphic & Design: Elke Hartleroad and M. G. Ron Johnson

MUSIC CREDITS

Creator and Producer: *Tony Salerno.* **Assistant Producers:** *Darek Dowgielewicz and C. Scott Votaw.*
Arrangers: *Darek Dowgielewicz, Christopher Carter, Guillermo Guzman, and Joe Ninowski.*
Writers: *Mark Collier, David Sparks, Paul Fischer, Mark Stitts, Ricardo "Tiki" Pasillas, Cindy Jordan,* and *Kim Sipus.*

Character Classics*™ *Teacher Activity Resource Book
ISBN Number: 1-931454-23-X
Published by Character Building Company
2246 Lindsay Way • Glendora, California 91740 • 1-800-310-7860
www.characterbuilding.com

Table of Contents

Attentiveness
at · tent' · tive · ness
Being carefully and sensibly aware of
the feelings, words, and needs of others.
"Pay attention and gain understanding."
-Proverbs

Composers

The following composers' melodies were used for the Attentiveness songs.

Ludwig van Beethoven

(bay´-toe´-vin)

Ludwig van Beethoven was born in Germany on December 16, 1770, and died on March 26, 1827, at the age of 57. His father, as well as his grandfather, were both operatic singers. At the age of 4, Ludwig's father began teaching him how to play the violin and by the time little Ludwig was 8, he was amazing everyone. As a teenager, he studied with such great composers as Franz Ries and even Wolfgang A. Mozart.

Franz Joseph Haydn

(high´-den)

Franz Joseph Haydn was born in lower Austria on March 31, 1732, and died on May 31, 1809, in Vienna. Joseph's father was an organist at the village church. Joseph's mother was a singer. Josef began to study music at the age of 5 and by the age of 13, he was writing music for the local churches.

Jacques Offenbach

(off´-in-bock´)

Jacques was born in Cologne, Germany, on June 21, 1819, and died in Paris on October 5, 1880. As a young man, he studied the cello at the Cologne Conservatory, then went to Paris to continue his work. He played in numerous orchestras and was best remembered as a writer of light opera.

Johann Strauss I

(strous)

Strauss was born in Vienna in 1804, and died there in 1849. He studied the violin and played the viola in a quartet when he was only 15. A the age of 24, he began to compose waltzes. He was the founder of the "Strauss Waltz Dynasty," as his sons became famous composers, also.

Peter Tchaikovsky

(chy-cough´-ski)

Peter Tchaikovsky, whose name can also be spelled Tschaikowsky, was born on May 7, 1840, and died November 6, 1893. He was known as one of the greatest Russian composers that ever lived. Peter didn't start out as a musician. He studied to be a lawyer, but at the age of 22, he took up music and in just three short years, he was writing award-winning compositions.

Lyrics

Little Larry

Orpheus in the Underworld
Allegretto Movement
Jacques Offenbach

Can can can you pay attention,
Do I have to mention
All the times you didn't listen,
Can you hear me?

Can can can you pay attention,
Do I have to mention
Everything I said, I'll say again!
(repeat)

Little Larry never listened
to a word his mother said,
She said walk and Larry ran,
he never seemed to understand
and
When she told him follow me,
he'd turn and walk the other
way,
Stop was go and go was stay,
I think I heard his mother say-

Can you hear me?
Listening is good for you,
Pay attention, maybe you'll
learn something new,
Little Larry, what am I to do with
you,
Larry, Larry, everything you
put me through!

Larry's mother's in the kitchen
baking up blueberry pies,
She said leave the pies alone,
but Larry couldn't figure why so
Larry ate the whole thing up
and now he's turned completely
blue,
Always listen to your mom
she knows a little more than
you!

Can you hear me?
Listening is good for you,
Pay attention, maybe you'll
learn something new,
Little Larry, what am I to do with
you,
Larry, Larry, now you've turned
completely blue!

Pay Attention

Symphony No. 9, 4th
Movement
Ode to Joy
Ludwig van Beethoven

Pay attention, listen children,
Heed the words I share today.
They'll keep you safe in times of
trouble,
Listen well, and then obey.

Treat each other with love and
kindness,
Always do right, and turn from
wrong.
Take my words and pay attention,
Hear the message of this song!

Listen to your moms and dads,
For words of wisdom they
impart.
They'll teach you how to treat
each other
And to love with all your heart.

Listen, children, listen closely,
Mom and Dad know what to do.
They'll guide you if you'll only
listen,
They know what is best for you!

Listen, children to your teachers
As they guide you while at
school.
Do your homework, read your
lessons.
Always keep the golden rule!

In the classroom,
While on the playground,
Help one another and be kind!
Keep these words and soon dis-
cover
You will have a brilliant mind!

Watch and Listen

Symphony No. 94, Second
Movement
Surprise Symphony
Franz Joseph Haydn

Never stand behind a mule,
Take a crocodile to school,
Never bathe an elephant
unless you have a pool.
Never swat an angry bee,
Chase a monkey up a tree,
Never sit beside a skunk,
no one will sit by you! Phew!

Watch and listen,
You could learn a lesson
and some good advice,
So watch and listen all day long,
Pay attention and you can't go
wrong.

Don't disturb a sleeping bear,
Ride an ostrich if you dare,
Never swim with hungry sharks
or dinner could be you! OOO!
Never grab a tiger's tail,
Try to catch a killer whale,
Never pet a porcupine,
surely you'll get poked! Ouch!

Watch and listen,
You could learn a lesson
and some good advice,
So watch and listen all day long,
Pay attention and you can't go
wrong.

Find a Friend

The Nutcracker Suite
Waltz of the Flowers
Peter Tchaikovsky

Sarah was rather sad
She had no one now to play with
She had just moved into a new
town
And her friends were nowhere to
be found
Starting a new school with lots
of boys and girls and teachers
with new faces!

Sarah felt all alone
No one to talk to, to laugh with
She wanted to hide and not be
found
She kept her eyes turned down
to the ground
This was such a scary day to
start school!
No one to be near her,
No one saw her shed a tear!

But suddenly a smiling face
approached her
(someone had seen her)
standing in the corner
(now they would greet her)
"Welcome to our school now
(my name is Brandon)
Would you be my friend today?

I saw you standing all alone
with sad eyes
(no one to talk to)
So I thought that I would
(come and be with you)
I know what it's like to
(be in a new school)
'Cause I'm new myself!
It's my first day too!"

Look around you,
Find someone new
Go ahead and share a kind word
Find a new friend,
Give a smile then,
This is how making friends
begins.

Look around you,
Find someone new
Go ahead and share a kind word
Find a new friend,
Give a smile then,

When you see someone sad
Sad, with nobody to talk with
Greet them with a warm and
friendly smile
Wear a grin that's wider than a
mile!
Pay attention to the needs of
others,
Spread a ray of sunshine.
Happiness is what you'll find.

Look around you,
Find someone new
Go ahead and share a kind
word.
Find a new friend,
Give a smile then,
Pay attention to others needs.

Goat on a Boat

Radetzky March
Johann Strauss I

Here's a tale you can tell if you
listen well,
'Bout a boat that's afloat on a
castle moat,
And aboard that boat there's a
Billy goat
in a grey overcoat, did I mention?
In the coat on the goat, is a one-
page note,

For the goat has a note that
his mother wrote,
And upon that note she wrote
All the following that I will
quote!

'What I bring to the King
is a diamond ring,
And the ring that I bring is for
marrying,
My son to your daughter,
Crossed over the water,
long he has sought her,
Your lovely daughter,
Oh, King, take the ring that I
gladly bring,
And all of the people will dance
and will shout and will sing!'

Well he looked at the goat
in the overcoat,
In a boat set afloat on a castle
moat,
And he held that note Billy's
mother wrote,
And the king cleared his throat,
and he said,

"I'm afraid, I must say,
that the goat can't stay,"
So the King told the goat
he should sail away,
And the reason why he did,
Little Billy Goat was just a kid!

Now you've heard every word
and the tale's complete,
Every word that you've heard,
you can now repeat,
Hope you listened through,
'cause it's up to you,
Do the very best that you can.

Word Search

Find and circle all of the words in the puzzle below. The words are listed below the puzzle. The first one has been circled for you.

A	R	H	E	E	D	F	U	L	U	N	B	P	I
W	T	E	L	F	V	O	E	I	O	C	N	A	W
A	U	T	G	T	C	M	K	S	Y	O	E	Y	O
R	A	B	E	A	I	D	B	T	L	B	K	I	A
E	M	S	R	N	R	K	A	E	P	S	V	N	C
T	W	E	N	M	T	D	G	N	T	E	D	G	O
R	E	S	L	P	I	I	N	W	J	R	Q	H	U
E	L	C	A	K	H	N	V	P	H	V	I	E	R
O	L	C	O	N	S	I	D	E	R	A	T	E	T
T	B	K	W	R	E	X	N	F	E	N	B	D	E
H	E	A	R	I	N	G	L	T	U	T	G	S	O
E	I	O	Z	M	S	F	H	M	E	L	P	R	U
R	N	Q	S	E	E	I	N	G	C	N	U	D	S
S	G	T	F	L	C	O	M	F	O	R	T	F	V

√1. ATTENTIVE
2. AWARE
3. CARE
4. COMFORT
5. CONSIDERATE
6. COURTEOUS
7. HEARING
8. HEEDFUL
9. INTENT
10. LISTEN
11. LOOK
12. MINDFUL
13. OBSERVANT
14. OTHERS
15. PAYING HEED
16. REGARD
17. SEEING
18. SENSE
19. SPEAK
20. WELL-BEING

Secret Message

Find the message that the plane is writing in the sky.

If you can follow the white smoke all the way up to the letter, write the letter in a box above the smoke.

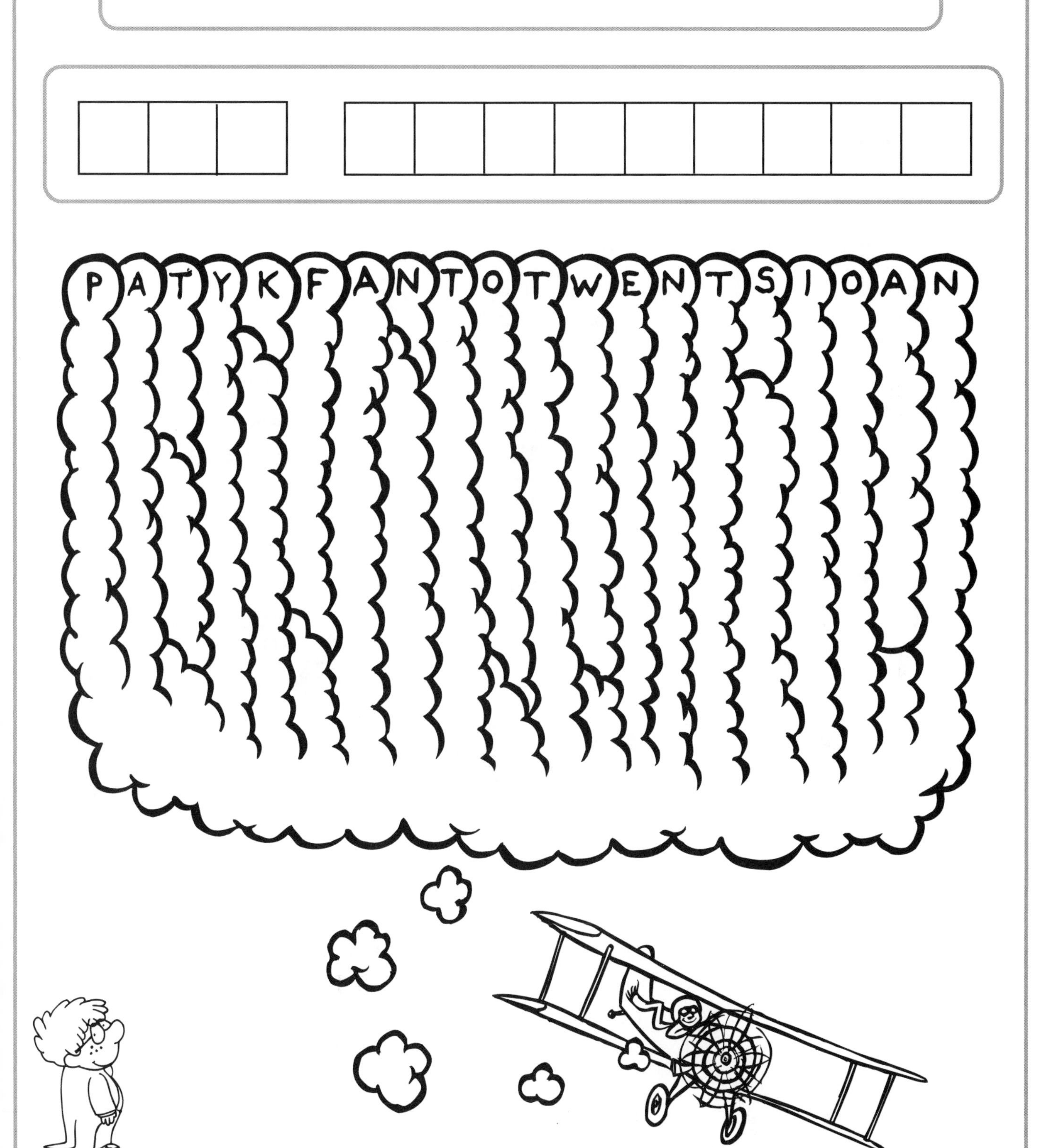

Picnic Path

Find the way to the picnic. Your teacher gave you directions to the school picnic in the park. Pay close attention to the clues and connect the dots.

1. Make your lunch.
2. Put it in the basket.
3. Pick up the butterfly net.
4. Walk to the school.
5. Pick some flowers.
6. Follow the rabbit to his hole.
7. Walk across the log.
8. Cross the bridge.
9. Stop at the stop sign.
10. Make a wish at the well.
11. Find the compass.
12. Go to the sign post. Unscramble the letters to see the way.

If I Listen

If I listen, I will know what to do.

In the box, write the number of the picture that the sentence is about.

❑ I will have to get up early on Mondays.

❑ Doctor's orders.

❑ I can't take my candy in there.

❑ Picnics are fun.

❑ I'll wear my raincoat today.

❑ After I finish raking leaves I will look under the doormat.

Pay Attention

Paying attention is not always listening to a person talk. There are other times we need to give our attention to be safe or to cooperate.

Look at each picture. Read the sentences below. Write the number of the picture that matches the sentence in the box.

- ☐ Should I wear my raincoat?
- ☐ Can I cross now?
- ☐ Nice dog!
- ☐ Maybe it is dry now.
- ☐ The grass looks so nice.
- ☐ Are there any cars coming?

Contentment

con · tent'ment

Being at peace with who you are
and what you have.

*"A contented heart is an even sea
in the midst of all storms."*

-Anonymous

Composers

The following composers' melodies were used for the Contentment songs.

Wolfgang Amadeus Mozart

(MOHT sart)

Mozart was born on January 27, 1756, in Salzburg, Austria, the son of Leopold Mozart, composer to the archbishop and a well-known violinist and author. He began playing the piano when he was three years old. From 1762 Leopold took young Mozart and his older sister, Maria Anna (called Nannerl), on tours throughout Europe in which they performed as harpsichordists and pianists, both separately and together. He is considered by some to be the greatest musical genius of all time. He died in Vienna on December 5, 1791.

Camille Saint-Saëns

(san-SAHNS)

Saint-Saëns was born in Paris, France, in 1835, and died in Algiers in 1921. He began composing when he was only 3 and wrote his first symphony at the age of 16. He was the first major composer to write music specifically for the cinema. Even though music was his first love, he was also interested in astronomy, archeology, philosophy, and even wrote poetry and essays. He composed over 300 works, including 13 operas.

Franz Schubert

(SHOO buhrt)

Schubert was born in the musical city, Vienna, Austria, on January 31, 1797, and died there on November 19, 1828. He was always poor and applied twice, without success, for a position for an orchestral conductor. He wrote several operas in an effort to earn money, but they were never performed. Even though he wrote many compositions, few were published during his lifetime. Now he is considered the greatest songwriter of all times.

Robert Schumann

(SHOO mahn)

Schumann was born in Germany on June 8, 1810, and died there on July 29, 1856, after a mental breakdown. His father was a translator of Romantic literature and Robert became one of the leading composers in the German Romantic period. He also became an influential music journalist. Some of his best work was written for his wife, Clara Wieck Schumann, a talented concert pianist.

Peter Tchaikovsky

(chy COFF skee)

Tchaikovsky, whose name can also be spelled Tschaikowsky, was born in Russia in 1840, and died there in 1893. He wrote some of the most beautiful music ever written. A shy man, he expressed his emotions in his music. He began taking lessons at the age of 7 and today is considered the greatest of all Russian composers.

Lyrics

Content With What You've Got

Eine Kleine Nachtmusik
Wolfgang Mozart

Chorus
Be content,
Content with what you've got,
Don't forget you've really got a lot!
Verse 1
Jenny went shopping at the store,
Had two she wanted four,
She's grabbing more and more,
Just look at Jenny,
Jenny has so many,
Others don't have any,
Jenny has so much!
Jenny, look around, settle down,
Stop that frown,
it doesn't look good on you,
You'll feel good inside, satisfied,
full of pride,
When you learn to...
Chorus
Be content, content with what you've got,
Don't forget you've really got a lot!
Verse 2
Billy, he thought he had it rough,
His room was full of stuff,
But that was not enough,
Just look at Billy, isn't Billy silly,
Really Billy, really,
Billy has so much!
Billy, look around, settle down,
Stop that frown, it doesn't look good on you,
You'll feel good inside, satisfied, full of pride,
When you learn to.....
Chorus
Be content, content with what you've got,
Don't forget you've really got a lot!
Be content, content with what you've got,
Don't forget you've really got a lot!
Verse 3
Sherri, she doesn't have a lot,
To her it matters not,
She's glad for what she's got,
Just look at Sherri,
Sherri is so very,
Extraordinary,
Sherri understands!
Take a look around, settle down,
Stop that frown, it doesn't look good on you,
You'll feel good inside, satisfied,
full of pride,
When you learn to.....
Chorus
Be content, content with what you've got,
Don't forget you've really got a lot!
Be content, content with what you've got,
Don't forget you've really got a lot!
Ending
You've got to be content,
You've got to be content with what you've got!

You're Special

Impromptu in A Flat Major,
Op. 90 No. 4
Franz Schubert

Verse 1
I may have a large nose,
And yours may be small,
Or maybe you're shorter,
And I'm extra tall,
Your hair may be curly,
And mine may be straight,
You may not have freckles,
But I have ninety-eight.
Verse 2
You may have a low voice,
And mine may be high,
You may be outgoing,
And I may be shy,
We're all very different,
Like each shining star,
So learn to be happy,
Content with who you are.
Chorus
You're special, I'm special,
The way that we are,
Believe that you're special,
And you will go far,
Be glad happy not sad,
Because you're special,
I'm special.
Verse 3
You may be an athlete,
And I may like art,
You put things together,
I take them apart,
We're all very different,
Like each shining star,
So learn to be happy,
Content with who you are.
Chorus
You're special, I'm special,
The way that we are,
Believe that you're special,
And you will go far,
Be glad happy not sad,
Because you're special,
I'm special.
We're all very different,
Like each shining star,
So learn to be happy,
Content with who you are.

Little Theodore

The Seasons - November
Peter Tchaikovsky

Chorus 1
Little Theodore, always wanting more,
Never satisfied, he is such a chore,
No one's ever seen him content before,
Always wanting more, little Theodore.
Chorus 2
I am Theodore, and I want some more,
I'm not satisfied, is it such a chore?
No one's ever seen me content before,
I want more and more
Just for me, little Theodore.
Verse 1
At the store little Theodore, something caught his eye,
Now he's squirming, pleading,
always needing,
Something new, not just one or two,
He wants three or four,
Theodore's grabbing, everything nabbing,
Poking and jabbing 'til he gets it!
Chorus 1
Little Theodore, always wanting more,
Never satisfied, he is such a chore,
No one's ever seen him content before,
Always wanting more, little Theodore.
Chorus 2
I am Theodore, and I want some more,
I'm not satisfied, is it such a chore?
No one's ever seen me content before,
I want more and more
Just for me, little Theodore.
Verse 2
Theodore at the ocean shore,
When it's time to go,
Theodore starts delaying, always saying,
"One more time, give me one last swim,
Let me go back in,"
Then he starts yelling, whining, and wailing,
Running and flailing 'till he gets to!
Chorus 1
Little Theodore, always wanting more,
Never satisfied, he is such a chore,
No one's ever seen him content before,
Always wanting more, little Theodore.

Last Chorus
And we won't be like little Theodore
Never satisfied, always wanting more.
Learn to be content, it's not such a chore,
Let's be satisfied, not like Theodore!
He wants more and more, little Theodore!

Edgar the Elephant

Le Carnaval des Animaux-L'Elephant
Camille Saint-Saens

Verse 1
My name is Edgar,
I never thought much of me,
I'm big and lumpy, kinda clumsy.
Very slow, can't even climb a tree,
Big ears, four big feet,
I've got a long windy nose,
I break all the toys and make lots of noise,
Wherever I goes.
Chorus
Now instead of what I can't do,
don't wanna be,
Concentrate on what I can do, who I can be,
I'm not the way I oughta be,
I'm gonna be content with me, now I see...
Verse 2
I'm big but I'm strong,
and I have incredible size,
To push and pull things,
lift and drag things,

Don't forget I'm very, very wise,
When I go swimming I always
make a big splash,
I spray like a hose and out of my nose,
A trumpet can blast!
Chorus
Now instead of what I can't do,
don't wanna be,
Concentrate on what I can do, who I can be,
I'm not the way I oughta be,
I'm gonna be content with me, now I see...
Verse 3
So listen to Edgar the elephant and you'll see,
It's not the can'ts and not the don'ts
But what we can do, who we all can be,
Thank you dear Edgar, for showing us,
That we all have special qualities,
And now I'll learn to be content with me!

My Memory Box

The Reaper's Song
Robert Schumann

Chorus 1
I have a box, filled with good memories,
I take it with me wherever I go,
Open it up and there's so much contentment,
These are the favorite memories I know.
Verse 1
The smell of fresh pop-corn,
a clown at the circus,
Some pink cotton candy, a hot dog and fries,
A ride on my bike through a giant mud puddle,
And friends at my house for
my birthday surprise.
Chorus 2
I have a box, filled with good memories,
Memories that take all my sadness away,
Open it up and there's so much contentment,
I fill it up with good memories each day.
Verse 2
A trip to the ocean, a perfect sand castle,
The wind in my hair and the sun on my face,
A triple scoop sundae that's smothered in chocolate,
The day Dad and I won a three-legged race.
Chorus 1
I have a box, filled with good memories,
I take it with me wherever I go,
Open it up and there's so much contentment,
These are the favorite memories I know.
Verse 3
Of camping and fishing on summer vacation,
The night before Christmas, I hardly can wait,
A cold winter night warming up by the fire,
A cup of hot chocolate and staying up late!
Chorus 2
I have a box, filled with good memories,
Memories that take all my sadness away,
Open it up and there's so much contentment,
I fill it up with good memories each day.
I fill it up with good memories each day.
Filling it up with good memories each day.

Find the Secret

Justin is always happy and whistling. Mark wondered what keeps Justin so happy. After being with Justin for a few days, Mark thinks he knows the answer.

Can you work Mark's puzzle and find the answer, too? Write the name of each item on the blanks. Copy the letter on the line above its number.

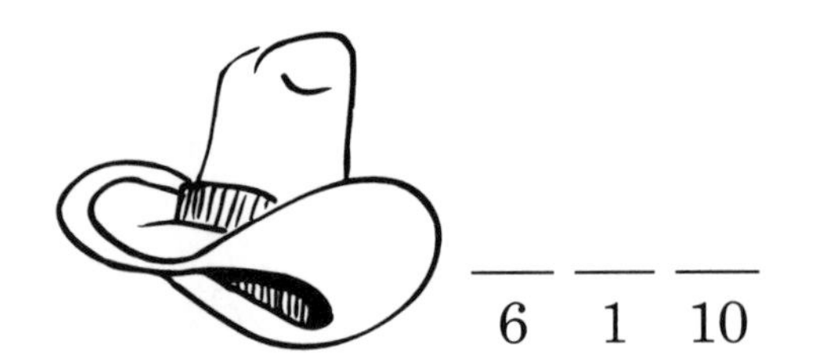

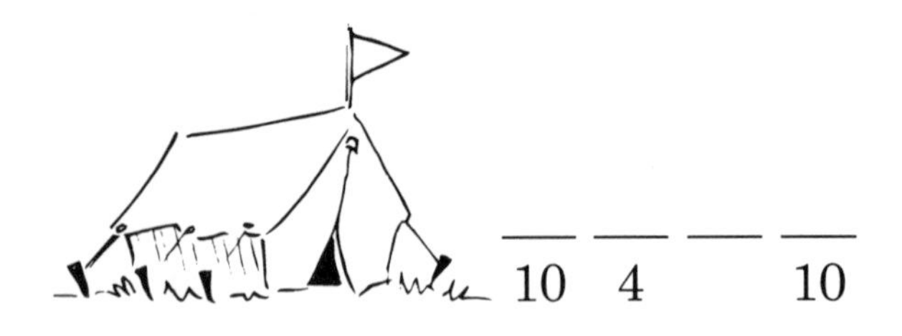

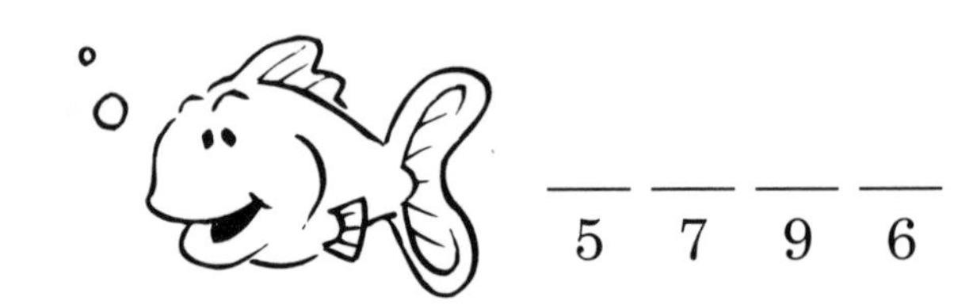

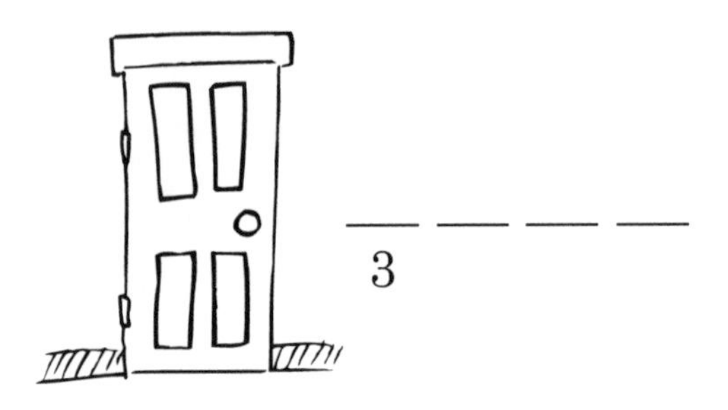

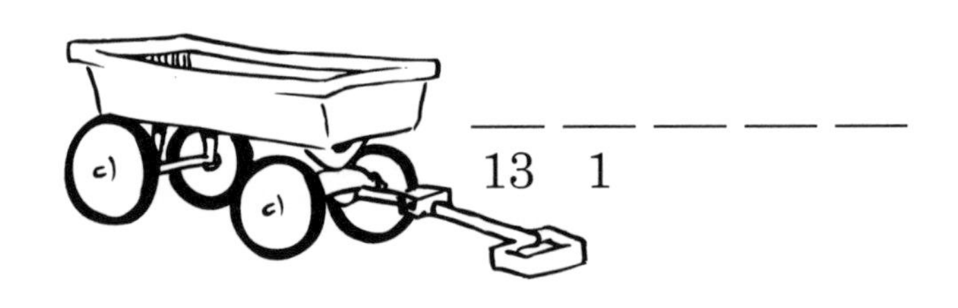

___ ___   ___ ___   ___ ___ ___ ___ ___ ___ ___ ___ ___
6 4   7 9   9 1 10 7 9 5 7 4 3

___ ___ ___ ___   ___ ___ ___ ___   ___ ___   ___ ___ ___ .
13 7 10 6   13 6 1 10   6 4   6 1 9

Word Search

Find and circle the words in the letter grid. They are words that describe a contented person. The words may be up, down, across, diagonal, or backwards.

C	A	L	M	N	E	S	S	O	F	G	N	H
A	O	O	U	E	A	E	A	L	N	L	O	E
P	R	N	S	F	R	E	W	U	U	A	I	L
L	N	E	T	E	E	R	S	F	D	D	T	P
E	S	L	N	E	S	C	Y	P	E	N	C	L
A	R	E	A	T	N	O	A	L	E	E	A	U
S	U	O	Y	O	J	T	H	E	P	S	F	F
A	W	O	E	O	I	E	M	H	P	S	S	R
N	E	D	L	E	G	R	E	E	A	A	I	E
T	T	L	N	H	A	R	M	O	N	Y	T	E
W	Y	C	G	N	I	T	S	U	R	T	A	H
O	E	H	A	P	P	I	N	E	S	S	S	C
L	U	F	K	N	A	H	T	S	A	O	W	A

1. CALMNESS
2. CHEERFUL
3. CONTENTMENT
4. GLADNESS
5. HAPPINESS
6. HARMONY
7. HELPFUL
8. JOLLY
9. JOYFUL
10. JOYOUS
11. MERRY
12. PATIENCE
13. PEACEFUL
14. PLEASANT
15. SATISFACTION
16. SERENE
17. THANKFUL
18. TRUSTING

A Secret Message

Look for these hidden things in the picture below:

1. It rhymes with ***cone***.
2. It rhymes with ***leg***.
3. It rhymes with ***bar***.
4. It rhymes with ***fowl***.
5. It rhymes with ***best***.
6. It rhymes with ***mop***.
7. It rhymes with ***beagle***.
8. It rhymes with ***pet***.
9. It rhymes with ***road***.

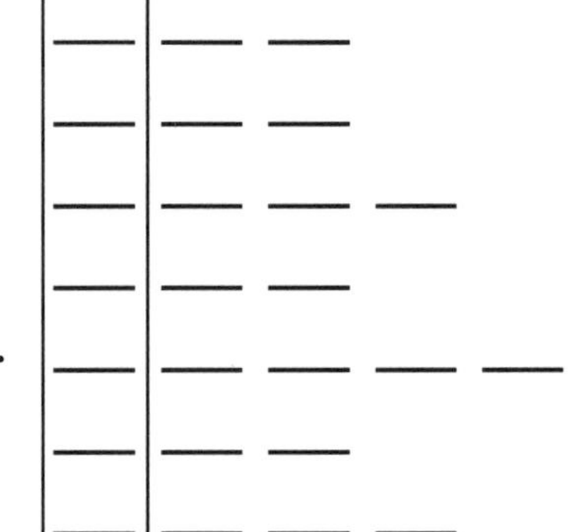

Now write, in order, the first letter in each word you wrote.

What is the message?

__ __   __ __ __ __ __ __ __ __ __.

Break the Code

Break the code and discover an important message. To find the answers use the Code Box to fill in the blanks with letters for each number.

CODE BOX

1	2	3	4	5	6	7	8	9	10	11	12	13	14	15	16	17	18	19	20	21	22	23	24	25	26
A	B	C	D	E	F	G	H	I	J	K	L	M	N	O	P	Q	R	S	T	U	V	W	X	Y	Z

Contentment is __ __ __ __ __ at
2 5 9 14 7

__ __ __ __ __ with __ __ __
16 5 1 3 5 23 8 15

__ __ __ __ __ __
25 15 21 1 18 5

and __ __ __ __
23 8 1 20

__ __ __ __ __ __ __ .
25 15 21 8 1 22 5

Can you think of three things that show you are a contented person?

1. ______________________________

2. ______________________________

3. ______________________________

Crossword Puzzle

Read the sentences, and find the word that will go in the blank. Use the words in the box. Then write the words in the crossword puzzle.

cheerful	envy	happy	help	joy	peaceful
dissatisfied	grateful	harmony	invites	merry	pleased

ACROSS

1. A contented person is ______.
4. When things go well together, they are in __________.
6. A happy person is _________.
8. To assist or be of use is to ________.
11. To be jealous is to _______.
12. A person who is not content is _______________.

DOWN

2. A calm person is ________.
3. To have pleasure is to have _______.
5. A joyous person is _______.
7. To be thankful is to be ___________.
9. To be satisfied is to be ___________.
10. Discontent __________ unhappiness.

Dependability
de · pend'a · bil'i · ty
Capable of being relied on or trusted in with full confidence regardless of circumstances.
"To be trusted (depended on) is a greater compliment than to be loved."
-George MacDonald
News

Composers

The following composers' melodies were used for the Dependability songs.

Johannes Brahms (BROMS)

Johannes was born in Hamburg, Germany, on May 7, 1833, and died April 3, 1897. He studied with his father, who was a double bassist in the Hamburg Theatre. By the age of 14, he was playing his own compositions in public. He is best remembered for his open-mindedness and great enthusiasm. Brahms was a greatly admired composer, even by those who opposed his style of music. Today he is considered one of the world's greatest composers, along with Bach and Beethoven.

Frédéric Chopin (shaw PAN)

Chopin was born in Poland in 1810 and died in Paris in 1849 at the age of 39 from tuberculosis. He was a child prodigy and his first polonaise was published at the age of 7. When he was 8 his brilliant piano technique captured the attention of audiences in Warsaw. By the time he was 20, he was already being called Poland's national composer. He left more music for the piano than any other composer in the history of music.

Charles Gounod (GOO noh)

Gounod was born in Paris on June 18, 1818, and died on October 10, 1893. He grew up in a cultured background. His mother was a distinguished pianist and his father was a talented painter, who died when his son was only 4 years old. Gounod's mother recognized his great ability and arranged for him to take music lessons. His most popular opera was *Faust*, which made him the most famous composer in France almost overnight.

Jacques Offenbach (AW fun bahk)

Offenbach was a French composer who was born in Cologne, Germany, in 1819 and died in Paris, France, in 1880. As a young man, he studied the cello at the Cologne Conservatory, then went to Paris to continue his work. He played in numerous orchestras and was best remembered as a writer of light opera.

Peter Tchaikovsky (chy COFF skee)

Tchaikovsky, whose name can also be spelled Tschaikowsky, was born in Russia in 1840 and died there in 1893. He is known as one of the greatest Russian composers of all times. However, Tchaikovsky didn't start out as a musician. He studied to be a lawyer, but at the age of 22, he took up music. A shy man, he put his emotions into his music. His melodies are considered to be some of the most beautiful in the world.

Lyrics

You Can Count on Me

Serenade for Strings in C Major, Waltz
Peter Tchaikovsky

Verse 1
Oh the sun will come out tomorrow,
Roll the tides up and
down by the sea,
And the moon and
the stars shining brightly.
These are some of the things
you can count on.
Just like you can depend on me!
Chorus
You can count on me, I'll do it,
I'll stick to it, I'll get through it,
If I set my mind to it I'm......
As sure as it's cold at the North
Pole, I have one goal,
I will never, never,
ever let you down,
I'll come through like heat in Hawaii,
No denying, I'll keep trying,
Count on me!
Verse 2
Like the flowers come up in the
springtime,
And a tree loses leaves in the fall,
Like a bear hibernates in the winter,
And the geese all fly north
in the summer,
You can count on me through it all!
Bridge
Any job you give me I will complete,
I'm definitely quick on my feet,
I'm so reliable, it's undeniable,
Call it dependability!
I'll be sure to give you
my guarantee,
You can even set your watches
by me,
I am always on time,
You don't have to remind,
Things are secure with me,
You can be sure of me,
Confident, trustworthy, yes you can
count on me!
Verse 3
Like a chicken lays eggs
each morning,
Like old faithful,
I always come through,
Like the thunder comes after the
lightning,
And the mail no matter the weather,
You can count on me, yes, it's true!
Chorus
You can count on me, I'll do it,
I'll stick to it, I'll get through it,
If I set my mind to it I'm......
I'm as sure as it's cold at the North
Pole, I have one goal,
That's to never, never,
ever let you down,
I'll come through like heat in Hawaii,
No denying, I'll keep trying,
Count on me!
Verse 4
And the sun will come out
tomorrow,
Roll the tides up and
down by the sea,
And the sun going
down happens nightly,
With the moon and
the stars shining brightly.
These are some of
the things you can count on.
Just like you can depend on me!

In a Minute

Minute Waltz, Op. 64, No. 1
Frederic Chopin

Verse 1
In a minute,
Yes, I mean it, in a minute,
That's the limit,
I will be there for you,
When it seems that everybody else
is late,
I will never ever make you wait!
Within a minute,
Never later alligator,
In a while crocodile, I will smile,
Not a second later, you will see,
I will show dependability.
Verse 2
I'm there when you call me.
Anytime you need me there,
Never stalling,
Right on time, believe me,
Never keep you waiting,
Never hesitating,
Taking just a minute,
Thoroughly committed,
There when you need me
There at your command,
I'm quick and I'm speedy,
Watch the second hand,
So this is my proposal,
I'm at your disposal,
You can always count on me!
Bridge
In a minute, in a flash,
A bolt of lightning, fire igniting me,
To your side I'll always dash,
Set your alarm by me,
Check your watch and you will see,
I'll be clockwise, my promptness
surprising,
I'm there in sixty seconds flat,
You can depend on me!
Verse 1
In a minute,
Yes, I mean it, in a minute,
That's the limit,
I will be there for you,
When it seems that
everybody else is late,
I will never ever make you wait!
Within a minute,
Never later alligator,
In a while crocodile, I will smile,
Not a second later, you will see,
I will show dependability.
Verse 2
I'm there when you call me.
Anytime you need me there,
Never stalling,
Right on time, believe me,
Never keep you waiting,
Never hesitating,
Taking just a minute,
Thoroughly committed,
There when you need me
There at your command,
I'm quick and I'm speedy,
Watch the second hand,
So this is my proposal,
I'm at your disposal,
You can always count on me!

Tardy Tim

Hungarian Dance #6 in Db Major
Johannes Brahms

Verse 1
Tardy the word that best
describes my friend Tim,
The one thing you should know
about him,
No matter what he does,
He's always late,
makes everybody wait,
Don't count him to be on time, he's
Tardy Tim.
Verse 2
Tardy, he's late for supper,
school and practice,
No matter where or when,
the fact is,
You can't depend on him
He's always late,
makes everybody wait,
Don't count him to be on time, he's
Tardy Tim.
Bridge 1
He's not a fast one,
Always the last one,
Tim isn't known for his punctuality!
No use depending,
Tardy is offending,
Always late, makes everybody wait,
Don't count him to be on time, he's
Tardy Tim.
Verse 3
One day, the baseball coach made
Tim a starter,
We thought he'd try a little harder,
How could we all forget?
He's always late, makes everybody
wait,
Don't count him to be on time, he's
Tardy Tim.
Verse 4
That day, they called the game,
we had to forfeit,
We learned a lesson, don't ignore it,
Because our team was late,
We lost the game,
And guess who was to blame,
Don't count on him to be on time,
he's Tardy Tim.
Bridge 1
He's not a fast one,
Always the last one,
Tim isn't known for his punctuality!
No use depending,
Tardy is offending,
Always late, makes everybody wait,
Don't count him to be on time, he's
Tardy Tim.
Bridge 2
Let's be the first ones,
Never be the last ones,
We'll all be known
for our punctuali—ty!
You can depend,
We never will offend,
We won't be late,
make everybody wait,
We'll be on time, never like him,
he's Tardy Tim!

Your Very Best Friend

Barcarolle from The Tales of Hoffman
Jacques Offenbach

I'm your friend, your very best
friend,
And you can depend on me.
Tried and true committed to you,
A friend I will always be.
Verse 1
When you need someone to talk to,
You can talk to me,
If you need a helping hand,
A helping hand I'll be,
And when you need to laugh,
I will laugh with you too,
And when you need to cry,
Here's my shoulder for you,
And if we're ever apart,
You have a place in my heart.
Chorus
I'm your friend, your very best
friend,
And you can depend on me.
Tried and true committed to you,
A friend I will always be.
Verse 2
Nothing else will come between us,
You're the friend I choose,
Always there to cheer you on,
No matter win or lose,
And when you call my name,
I will be there for you,
Each promise that I make,
I will always come through,
And if we're ever apart,
You have a place in my heart.
Chorus
I'm your friend,
your very best friend,
And you can depend on me.
Tried and true committed to you,
A friend I will always be.
Ending
I'm your very best friend,
I'll be there to the end,
You can always depend,
On your very best friend.

Dependable Ants

(Worker Ants' Chorus)
Soldier's Chorus from Faust
Charles Gounod

Chorus
We are dependable worker ants,
Helping each other we have a
chance,
Working together we will advance,
We work as a team, You'll see what
I mean,
Dependable ants.
(repeat Chorus)
Verse 1
One by one we will all do our best,
Building, working, defending the
nest,
Each collecting the food for the rest,
We're marching in line, And every-
thing's fine,
Dependable ants.
Chorus
We are dependable worker ants,
Helping each other we have a
chance,
Working together we will advance,
We work as a team, You'll see what
I mean,
Dependable ants.
Verse 2
If there's ever a river too wide,
Arm in arm we can reach the other
side,
Each one giving to the other a ride,
Whatever it takes, Commitment to
make,
Dependable ants.
Chorus
We are dependable worker ants,
Helping each other we have a
chance,
Working together we will advance,
We work as a team, You'll see what
I mean,
Dependable ants.
Verse 3
We are really a big family,
Each ant helping the whole colony,
That's the way we can live happily,
More work to be done, Together it's
fun,
Dependable ants.
Last Chorus
Just like dependable worker ants,
Helping each other we have a
chance,
Working together we will advance,
Let's work as a team, You'll see
what I mean. Dependable ants.
Let's work as a team, You'll see
what I mean. Dependable ants.

Can You Depend on It?

There are some things that you can depend on or count on to happen. Then there are other things that you cannot depend on. Look at each picture below. If you can depend on it, circle the YES. If you cannot depend on it, circle the NO.

Can you depend on:

YES NO

The sun rising and setting

YES NO

A cat to stop scratching

YES NO

The weather to always be sunny

YES NO

School starting every year

YES NO

A baby not to cry

YES NO

The leaves falling from the trees

Word Search

Find and circle the following words in the puzzle below. The words may read up, down, across, or diagonal. The first one is circled for you.

T	A	E	V	E	I	L	E	B	A	I	E	L	N
O	T	R	U	T	H	A	A	O	R	B	B	T	E
Y	T	U	D	R	O	A	E	L	B	A	T	S	A
C	A	S	E	U	N	D	F	M	A	N	O	A	T
O	D	L	E	T	E	A	R	I	W	O	W	F	N
N	Y	E	Y	E	S	I	M	O	R	P	J	D	E
F	E	D	P	U	T	U	V	E	W	M	E	A	T
I	L	P	A	E	C	A	R	E	F	U	L	E	S
D	B	I	D	E	N	O	X	T	R	O	S	T	I
E	A	G	O	L	T	D	Y	D	I	L	O	S	S
N	I	A	E	E	Y	S	L	L	O	Y	A	L	N
C	L	R	R	M	F	A	I	T	H	F	U	L	O
E	E	T	N	E	M	T	I	M	M	O	C	L	C
D	R	E	T	N	A	T	S	N	O	C	Z	Q	A

1. ~~BELIEVE~~
2. CAREFUL
3. COMMITMENT
4. CONFIDENCE
5. CONSISTENT
6. CONSTANT
7. DEPEND
8. DUTY
9. FAITHFUL
10. FIRM
11. HONEST
12. LOYAL
13. PROMISE
14. RELIABLE
15. RELY
16. SOLID
17. STABLE
18. STEADFAST
19. STEADY
20. SURE
21. TRUST
22. TRUTH
23. VOW
24. WORD

Crossword Puzzle

accountable	depend	loyal	rely	trustworthy
believe	honest	promise	truthful	

ACROSS

1. Someone who doesn't lie is this.
2. "Really" minus the "al."
3. You can "count" on me.
4. I am "full of truth."

DOWN

1. To make an oath or pledge.
2. "Deep" minus an "e" plus "end."
3. I am "worth of your trust."
4. I will always be your friend.
5. To have faith or trust in someone.

Missing Letters

Using the clues on the left, fill in the missing letters in the words below. The missing letters will spell a word. Copy the letters on the blanks to complete the sentence.

I believe in you.	T _ U S T
You will be there when I need you.	D _ P E N D
You do not lie. You are honest.	T R U T H F U _
I am sure; yes, I'm sure!	C O N F _ D E N T
I can predict what you will do. You keep your promises.	P R E D I C T _ B L E
I can count on you.	A C C O U N T A _ L E
You are a true friend.	L O Y A _
You always tell the truth.	H O N _ S T

If you are a _ _ _ _ _ _ _ _ _ person, people can depend on you.

What kinds of things can you do to let people know that they can rely on you?

1. ______________________________

2. ______________________________

3. ______________________________

Alphabet Code

Break the code and discover an important message. Match the letter below the blank with another letter in the Code Box. Write the correct letter on the blank.

CODE BOX

A	B	C	D	E	F	G	H	I	J	K	L	M	N	O	P	Q	R	S	T	U	V	W	X	Y	Z
Z	Y	X	W	V	U	T	S	R	Q	P	O	N	M	L	K	J	I	H	G	F	E	D	C	B	A

Dependability is when you are _ _ _ _ _ _ _
X Z K Z Y O V

of being _ _ _ _ _ _ on or
I V O R V W

_ _ _ _ _ _ _ in with full
G I F H G V W

_ _ _ _ _ _ _ _ _ _ regardless of
X L M U R W V M X V

_ _ _ _ _ _ _ _ _ _ _ _ _
X R I X F N H G Z M X V H

Name three ways that show you can be depended on:

1. ______________________________
2. ______________________________
3. ______________________________

Goodness
good' · ness
Being well-behaved, mannerly, and kind; doing what is right and proper.
"You can only make others better by being good yourself."

Composers

The following composers' melodies were used for the Goodness songs.

Ludwig van Beethoven

(bay´-toe´-vin)

Beethoven was born in Germany in 1770, and died in 1827. He began playing the violin at age four. He studied with many greats such as Mozart and Haydn. He had a great influence on the history and development of music. His music is performed more than any other composer.

Georges Bizet

(bee-zay´)

Alexandre César Léopold Bizet (known as Georges) was born in Paris, France on October 25, 1838, and died in Bougival on June 3, 1875. At the age of 9, he entered the Paris Conservatory of Music. He won numerous awards and was best remembered for his operas. He often wrote comic opera, but was best known for the opera *Carmen*. He died 3 months after it opened.

Wolfgang Amadeus Mozart

(moats´-art)

Mozart was born in Austria in 1756 with the name Johannes Chrysostomus Wolfgangus Theophilus Mozart and died in 1791. He began to play the piano when he was three years old. By the age of six he had become an accomplished performer on the clavier, violin, and organ. He is considered by some to be the greatest musical genius of all time.

Giuseppe Verdi

(vair´-dee)

Verdi was born in Italy in 1813 and died in 1901. He was Italy's foremost composer of operas. As a child he showed great interest in all kinds of music. His operas are among the most frequently produced in the world today.

Antonio Vivaldi

(veh-vall´-dee)

Vivaldi was born in 1678 and died in 1741. His works include more than 500 concertos and over 70 sonatas and about 45 operas and religious music. He was the most influential Italian composer and violinist of his age.

Lyrics

Danny's Good Adventure

La Donna e Mobile

Giuseppe Verdi

It was hard to be good
In Danny's neighborhood,
Lots of bad drugs and fights
Crimes almost every night,
But still he tried his best,
To rise above the rest,
Made it to school each day,
While others stayed away,
Danny heard their bragging,
Put up with their ragging,
He would find a way—
To start a new life!

A new life, a new life,
To start a new life,
To start a new life.

So Danny studied hard,
And he earned his reward,
Worked at a steady clip,
He won a scholarship,
He always kept in line
Tried to be good and kind,
He became Doctor Dan,
A well-respected man,
He tried hard to be good
And to do what he should.
Danny found a way—
To make a new life!

A new life, a new life,
To make a new life,
He tried hard to be good
And to do what he should.
Danny found a way—
To make a new life!

The Frog on a Log

La Primavera from the Four Seasons

Antonio Vivaldi

Said buzzing bee to the frog,
Who was sitting there on a log,
"Little frog on the log down in the bog
It may be simply a hunch,
But before you eat me for lunch,
There is something you need to know."

Chorus
Take one little look behind you,
I'm sure that it will remind you,
That you should be good to me,
And maybe the good that you do,
Is finding its way back to you

So will you be good to me?
Said frog to the big crocodile,
Who was swimming by with a smile,
"Crocodile with a smile, just wait awhile,

I know you're licking your chops,
For a little froggy that hops,
But there's something you need to know."

Chorus
Take one little look behind you,
I'm sure that it will remind you,
That you should be good to me,
And maybe the good that you do,
Is finding its way back to you
So will you be good to me?

Said crocodile to the man,
Hunting crocodiles was his plan,
"Hunting man with a plan, please understand,
But before you do what you do,
And send me off to the zoo,
There is something you need to know."

Chorus
Take one little look behind you,
I'm sure that it will remind you,
That you should be good to me,
And maybe the good that you do,
Is finding its way back to you
So will you be good to me?

Said hunting man to the bee
Who was buzzing now in the tree,
"I'm allergic to buzzing bees you see,
Before you give me a sting,
And the swelling that it will bring,
There is something you need to know."

Chorus
Take one little look behind you,
I'm sure that it will remind you,
That you should be good to me,
And maybe the good that you do,
Is finding its way back to you
So will you be good to me?

In Your Heart

Sonata No. 8 in C Minor, Op. 13 Pathetique Sonata-Adagio Cantabile Movement

Ludwig van Beethoven

Chorus
In your heart that's where all good things start,
Your good thoughts become good words,
Good things you do for others.
Keep it true, the good inside of you,
Protect it and respect it,
Let goodness grow in your heart.

Each day you fill your heart,
Be careful what you put inside it,
Choose the right things, far away from wrong,
Then the good will stay alive inside your heart,
And other people see the good that grows inside of you
And you can see the good inside of other people, too.

In your heart, that's where all good things start,
Your good thoughts become good words,
Good things you do for others.
Each day you fill your heart,
Be careful what you put inside it,
Choose the right things, far away from wrong.
Then the good will stay alive inside your heart.

In your heart, that's where all good things start,
Your good thoughts become good words,
Good things you do for others.
Keep it true, the good inside of you,
Protect it and respect it,
Let goodness grow in your heart

The Party

Habañera from *Carmen*

Georges Bizet

My dear mama she said to me,
"Tonight we're going to have a big party,
It's important that you behave,
Or you will send me to an early grave!

"Not like last year, you made a mess,
You spilled your dinner on that lady's dress,
Bumped the waiter, he dropped the cake,
And then you brought out Freddy, your pet snake,

"Things will not be the same tonight,
You'll learn some manners, you will be polite,
This year's party will be your last,
Unless you learn a little goodness fast!"

Chorus
Will you be good? I will be good!
Will you be good because you know you should?
Will you be good? I will be good!
All right then, very well, it's understood,
You will be good? I will be good,
I will be good because I know I should!
You will be good? Yes, I'll be good!
I will be good, it is understood!
Be Good!

So the people they filled our house,
But I kept quiet as a tiny mouse,
No dropped dinner and no dropped cake,
And most importantly no Fred the Snake,

I was really a model child,
A perfect angel, not my normal wild,
Once was bad, but I made the switch,
And so the party went without a glitch.

Now my mama she knows it's true,
I've learned my lesson, I know what to do,
Next year's party will be the best,
'Cause mama knows I passed the goodness test!

When Everyone Is Watching

Rondo alla Turca
from *A major Sonata*

Wolfgang Amadeus Mozart

Valerie is good, very, very good.
Valerie does everything exactly as she should.
Yes, when everyone is watching her, she's really very good,
Helpful and polite, intelligent and bright,
Valerie is charming, what they call a pure delight.
Yes, she's really quite an angel, that's until she leaves your sight,
When she knows that nobody can see,
Then a different Valerie she'll be.

Now she's not polite, doesn't act so bright,
Valerie's no longer what you call a pure delight,
No, she's really not an angel when she's out of sight.
And you really never, never know,
Is it real or putting on a show?
Is it just a game? Can you be the same?
Why is it that always being good is such a strain?
Don't let all the good things that you do go down the drain!

Chorus
She is good, she is very good when everyone is watching.
She is bad, very bad when everybody turns away.
Let's be good, very good, when everyone is watching,
Let's be good, better yet, when everybody turns away!

Jeremy is good, very, very good.
Jeremy does everything exactly as he should.
Yes, when everyone is watching him he's really very good,

Courteous and sweet, really quite a treat,
Jeremy is practically the finest boy you'll meet,
And he seems a perfect angel, but the story's not complete.
When he knows that nobody can see,
Then a different Jeremy he'll be.

Now he's not so sweet, really not a treat,
Jeremy is someone that you wouldn't want to meet.
No, he's not the perfect angel when it's all complete
And you really never know,
'Cause he's always putting on a show,
Is it just a game? Can you be the same?
Why is it that always being good is such a strain?
Don't let all the good things that you do go down the drain!

Chorus
He is good, he is very good when everyone is watching.
He is bad, very bad when everybody turns away.
Let's be good, very good, when everyone is watching,
Let's be good, better yet, when everybody turns away!

Code Busters

Good George wants you to know something about goodness. Solve the puzzle below by matching the code below the blanks with the letter in the Code box. Write the correct letter in the blanks.

	1	2	3	4
A	O	T	D	I
B	A	E	F	L
C	G	B	C	H
D	M	R	N	S

___ ___ ___   ___ ___ ___ ___   ___ ___ ___ ___
A1 D3 B2   C1 A1 A1 A3   A3 B2 B2 A3

___ ___ ___ ___ ___ ___   ___ ___ ___ ___ ___
C2 D2 A4 D3 C1 D4   B3 A1 D2 A2 C4

___ ___ ___ ___ ___ ___ ___
B1 D3 A1 A2 C4 B2 D2

Bonus Question: What do you think this means?

____

Name a time when you did a good deed which caused someone else to do a good deed.

____

____

Break the Code

Break the code and discover an important message. To find the answers use the Code Box to fill in the blanks with letters for each number.

CODE BOX

1	2	3	4	5	6	7	8	9	10	11	12	13	14	15	16	17	18	19	20	21	22	23	24	25	26
A	B	C	D	E	F	G	H	I	J	K	L	M	N	O	P	Q	R	S	T	U	V	W	X	Y	Z

Goodness is ___ ___ ___ ___ ___
2 5 9 14 7

___ ___ ___ ___ – ___ ___ ___ ___ ___ ___ ___ ,
23 5 12 12 2 5 8 1 22 5 4

___ ___ ___ ___ ___ ___ ___ ___ , and
13 1 14 14 5 18 12 25

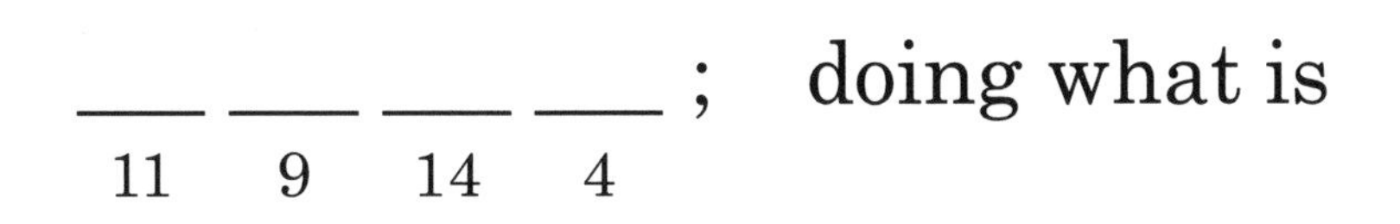

___ ___ ___ ___ ; doing what is
11 9 14 4

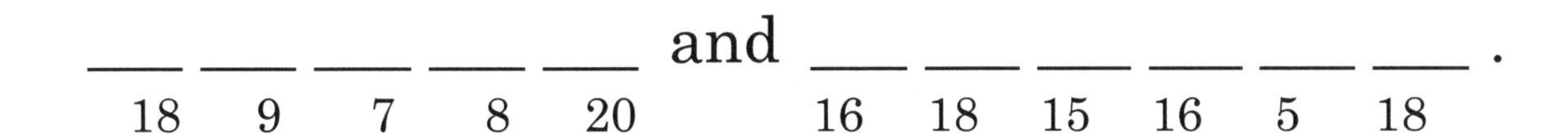

___ ___ ___ ___ ___ and ___ ___ ___ ___ ___ ___ .
18 9 7 8 20 16 18 15 16 5 18

Name three ways that you can show goodness.

1.______________________________

2.______________________________

3.______________________________

Crossword Puzzle

Write the correct word in the blank. Then write the word in the puzzle. The words are listed in the box below.

honest	mercy	orderly	polite	true
kindness	merit	pleasant	real	

ACROSS

1. Kind words _____________ a friendly response.
4. A person's smile tells his _____________ feelings.
5. Keep your room _____________ .
7. Tell the truth; be _____________ .
8. Show _____________ to those in trouble.

DOWN

1. Have _____________ on people in need.
2. Don't be false, be _____________ .
3. If you are _____________ people will enjoy being around you.
6. Have good manners, be _____________ .

1. 2. 3. 4. 5. 6. 7. 8.

Goodness Meal

Which of the items below would you have in a "goodness meal"? Write the ones you select on the menu below. Why not put a price beside each item such as two hugs or one smile?

happy hamburger	cruelty cola
bitterness biscuits	courteous custard
thoughtful tamales	anger applesauce
praises punch	polite pudding
put-down pie	hate hot dogs
kindness cake	teasing tea
compliment cookies	jealous jelly
belligerent bananas	mannerly muffins

The Goodness Menu

happy hamburger $ one hug	______ $ ______
______ $ ______	______ $ ______
______ $ ______	______ $ ______
______ $ ______	______ $ ______

Maze for the Answer

Find a special message in the maze below. First, go through the maze until you find the end. Then go back and circle every other letter starting with the first one. Copy the circled letters on the blanks below and you will see the special message.

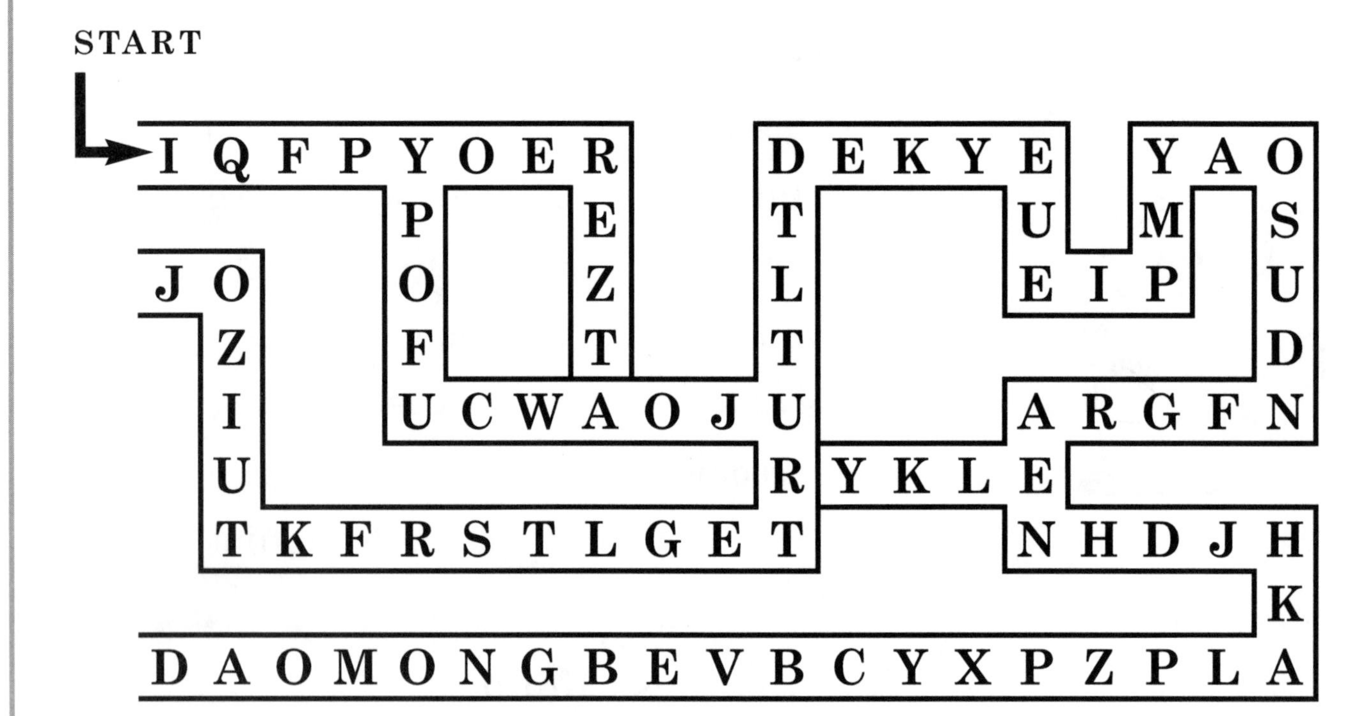

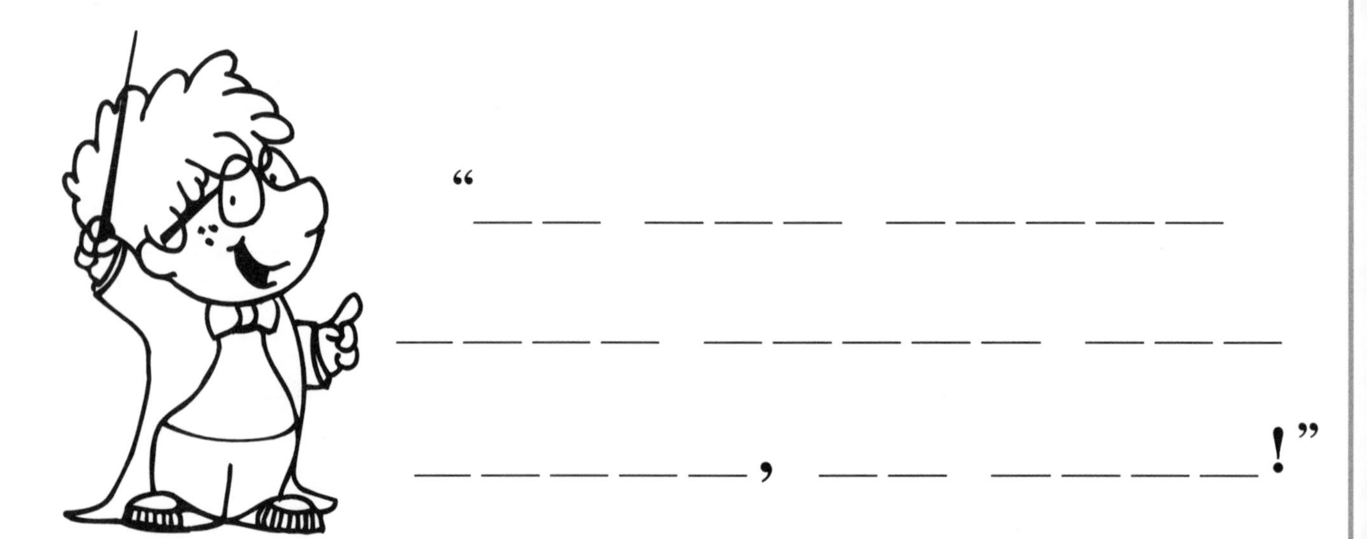

Kindness
kind' · ness
An act of love that adds to
the true happiness of others.
"A kind word is like a spring day."
-Russian Proverb
SEEDS
DOGGIE

Composers

The following composers' melodies were used for the Kindness songs.

Johann Sebastian Bach

(bock)

Johann Sebastian Bach was born in Germany on March 21, 1685, and died July 28, 1750. The son of another famous composer/musician, Johann Ambrosius Bach, he had great promise as a composer from an early age. Devastated by his parents' death, at the age of 10, he went to live with his brother who taught him to play the clavichord. His career started, when at the age of 15, his soprano voice placed him in the St. Michael's choir in Luneburg. He is recognized as one of the greatest composers that ever lived. Some call him the "Father of Music."

Ludwig van Beethoven

(bay´-toe´-vin)

Ludwig van Beethoven was born in Germany on December 16, 1770, and died on March 26, 1827, at the age of 57. His father, as well as his grandfather, were both operatic singers. At the age of 4, Ludwig's father began teaching him how to play the violin. By the time little Ludwig was 8, he was amazing everyone. As a teenager, he studied with such great composers as Franz Ries and even Wolfgang A. Mozart.

Antonin Dvořák

(da-vore´-zhock´)

Antonin Dvorák was born in Bohemia on September 8, 1841. He was one of the most well-known Bohemian composers in history. Born the son of an inn-keeper, his father wanted him to be a butcher. The local schoolmaster taught him to play the violin. At the age of 16, he entered the Prague Orchestra School and made his living playing in a small orchestra. He started his serious composing at the age of 33, but it wasn't until 1875 that he acquired enough support to devote the rest of his life to composition. He died in Prague on May 1, 1904.

Albert Elmenreich

(el-men-rike)

Albert Elmenreich was born in Germany on February 10, 1816, and died on May 30, 1905, at the ripe old age of 89 years. He was trained as an actor and worked primarily at the Theatre in Schwerin. He composed many operas from 1849 until his death.

Peter Tchaikovsky

(chy-cough´-ski)

Peter Tchaikovsky, whose name can also be spelled Tschaikowsky, was born on May 7, 1840, and died November 6, 1893. He was known as one of the greatest Russian composers that ever lived. Peter didn't start out as a musician. He studied to be a lawyer, but at the age of 22, he took up music and in just three short years, he was writing award-winning compositions.

Georges Bizet

(bee-zay´)

Alexandre César Léopold Bizet (known as Georges) was born in Paris, France on October 25, 1838, and died in Bougival on June 3, 1875. At the age of 9, he entered the Paris Conservatory of Music. He won numerous awards and was best remembered for his operas. He often wrote comic opera, but was best known for the opera *Carmen*. He died 3 months after it opened.

Lyrics

Show a Little Kindness

Spinning Song
Albert Elmenreich

Show a little kindness each day,
In all that you do and say.
Lend a helping hand as you play,
Spread a seed of joy in your way.

And you will bring
Smiles to every face each day
And you'll make the world a better place!

Spread a seed of joy in your way,
Lend a helping hand as you play.
In all that you do and you say,
Show a little kindness each day.

Be a true friend
Through thick and thin
Caring and kind
All of the time.

Make everyday
Better some way
Tell all your friends
Kindness will win!

Show a little kindness each day,
In all that you do and say.
Lend a helping hand as you play,
Spread a seed of joy in your way.

And you will bring
Smiles to every face each day
And you'll make the world a better place!

Spread a seed of joy in your way,
Lend a helping hand as you play.
In all that you do and say,
Show a little kindness each day.

Kindness Every Day

Turkish March
Ludwig van Beethoven

Kindness is the golden rule,
Fill up the cup of kindness till it's full.
Share a smile along the way,
Be kind to others every day!

Care a little
Care a lot and
Make this world
A better spot by

Kindness, kindness, every day,
So share a drop of love along the way.
Keep the golden rule each day,
And you will show the world the way!

Duck and Gator

Anna Magdalena Bach Notebook Musette
Johann Sebastian Bach

Kind alligator, sweet alligator,
'Reckon I'll have myself some dinner.
Nice alligator, dear alligator,
Get me some duckling on my plate.
Big alligator, strong alligator,
One that is plump, not many feathers.
Smart alligator, good alligator,
Over here, duck, don't make me wait!

Beautiful reptile of the swamp,
You are king and I am just a duckling,
You are so quick and clever,
Can't we be friends forever,
All the other animals around
will want to be your friend, too.
Is that really true?

Kind alligator, sweet alligator,
What am I going to do for dinner?
Nice alligator, dear alligator,
Guess I'll go back to leaves and sticks.

Big alligator, strong alligator,
Nobody else has ever liked me,
Smart alligator,
Hey, little ducky, let' s be friends!

Melody of Kindness

Humoresque No. 7
Antonin Dvoˇrák

When I'm kind, it's plain to see
That others will be kind to me
And that's how I remember to be kind.

If you're kind in what you do,
Then people will be kind to you,
Remember this and you'll be kind.

O do a good deed,
And plant a kind seed!
Let kindness be found all around
And when you share a kind deed
Then you will see
Kindness growing,
Kindness flowing all around!

I'm Only a Tree

March from The Nutcracker Suite
Peter Tchaikovsky

I'm only a tree,
be kind to me,
I'm only a tree,
be kind to me.

My name is Pete,
I am a pine,
Been standing here the longest time,
I'm big, I'm green,
I'm tall, I'm clean,
I want to be your friend.

I smell the best of any tree,
I'll give you all my cones for free,
Don't let them chop me down,
I'm more than just good wood!

I'm only a tree, be kind to me,
I'm only a tree, be kind to me.

My name is Ed, I am an oak,
I'm from a line of friendly folk,
I'm big and strong and beautiful,
I want to be your friend.

I give you shade and oxygen,
My leaves protect you from the wind,
I'm good for climbing, building forts,
Or hang a swing from me.

I'm only a tree, be kind to me,
I'm only a tree, be kind to me.

My name is Paula palm,
With other trees I have no qualm,
But I'm as different as can be,
I want to be your friend.

I'm tall and thin with lots of hair,
Sometimes there are coconuts up there,
I don't need much attention,
Just sit back and watch me grow.
I'm only a tree, be kind to me.

Captain Kind

From the Opera Carmen
The Toreadors
Georges Bizet

Faster than lightning,
come to save the day,
Able to chase anger away,
He can stop a fight before it starts,
Turn that bad into good.

A friend to everyone,
A friend of mine,
Hooray for Captain Kind!

Billy the Bully, boy, he's really bad,
I've had enough, he makes me mad!
I recall the Captain's good advice,
Always best to be kind.

Now Billy has become
A friend of mine,
Hooray for Captain Kind!

My older sister's always on my nerves,
I'll see she gets what she deserves.
Captain to the rescue just in time,
Helping me to be kind!

My sister has become
A friend of mine,
Hooray for Captain Kind!

Use the Right Bait

Can you catch someone with kindness?

Which hook will catch the fish? Draw a line from the hook with the bait sign to the fish that it will catch.

Word Search

Find and circle all of the words in the puzzle below. The words are listed below the puzzle. The words may read across, down, backwards, or diagonally. The first one has been circled for you.

C	O	N	C	E	R	N	G	S	U	F	C	W	D
H	D	G	C	O	N	S	I	D	E	R	A	T	E
F	T	O	L	E	R	A	N	T	Z	I	R	A	T
L	H	I	B	M	K	Y	L	U	T	E	I	Q	R
J	O	E	G	N	I	R	A	H	S	N	N	E	A
E	U	V	T	E	N	D	E	R	K	D	G	H	E
L	G	N	E	C	D	W	Y	O	X	L	X	A	H
B	H	E	K	Y	H	T	A	P	M	Y	S	P	D
A	T	P	N	L	E	O	N	R	Z	U	A	P	O
E	F	M	I	E	A	Q	C	H	M	P	F	I	O
E	U	N	D	E	R	S	T	A	N	D	I	N	G
R	L	A	B	F	T	O	L	U	F	P	L	E	H
G	E	N	T	L	E	R	U	J	V	G	T	S	W
A	S	K	I	N	D	N	E	S	S	B	D	S	C

√ 1. AGREEABLE
2. CARING
3. CONCERN
4. CONSIDERATE
5. FRIENDLY
6. GENEROUS
7. GENTLE
8. GOODHEARTED
9. HAPPINESS
10. HELPFUL
11. KINDHEARTED
12. KINDNESS
13. LOVE
14. SHARING
15. SYMPATHY
16. TENDER
17. THOUGHTFUL
18. TOLERANT
19. UNDERSTANDING
20. WARM

Word Puzzle

Circle each word in the puzzle from the Word Box.

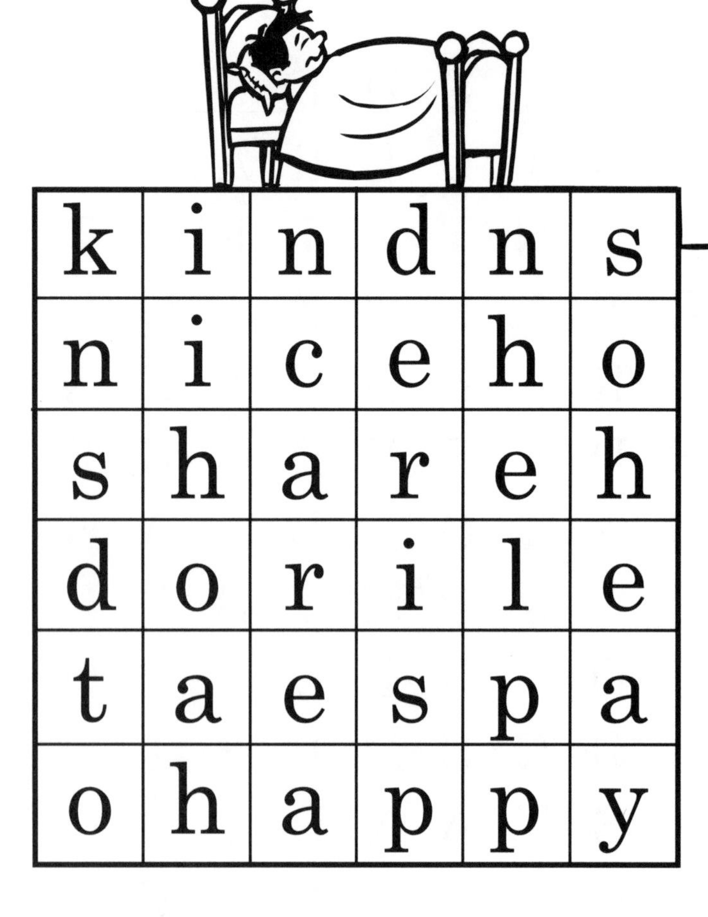

k	i	n	d	n	s
n	i	c	e	h	o
s	h	a	r	e	h
d	o	r	i	l	e
t	a	e	s	p	a
o	h	a	p	p	y

help
kind
share
nice
happy
care

Write the correct word in the blanks.

1. Always be ______________________.
2. __________________ your toys.
3. Be ______________ to others.
4. ______________ for those in need.
5. When you are kind you make others _______________.
6. When you ___________ others you are showing kindness.

Words of Kindness

The words we say can be acts of kindness or acts of unkindness. Read the words below. Put a check in the correct box.

"Your dress is pretty."

❑ Kind ❑ Unkind

"Would you like a push?"

❑ Kind ❑ Unkind

"Look at those skinny legs."

❑ Kind ❑ Unkind

"Let me help you with this."

❑ Kind ❑ Unkind

"We don't want you on our team."

❑ Kind ❑ Unkind

"Your hair looks awful."

❑ Kind ❑ Unkind

REMEMBER: A KIND WORD IS LIKE A SPRING DAY!

Show Kindness

Find something that we should be kind to. Solve the problems below. Then match the letters and the answers to the numbers on the lines below.

56 + 22 = __ I	29 - 12 = __ W	19 + 19 = __ T	48 - 29 = __ E	72 - 16 = __ D
15 - 11 = __ M	67 + 23 = __ B	85 - 17 = __ G	34 - 18 = __ A	54 + 33 = __ K
82 + 12 = __ S	43 - 22 = __ N	61 + 19 = __ O	27 + 16 = __ J	75 - 69 = __ L

__ __   __ __ __ __   __ __
90 19   87 78 21 56   38 80

__ __ __ __ __ __ __ .
16 21 78 4 16 6 94

Obedience
o·be'·di·ence
Responding to the wishes or commands of those in authority who care for me.
"He who would command others must learn to obey."
TRASH

Composers

The following composers' melodies were used for the Obedience songs.

Thomas Haynes Bayly

(bay´-lee)

Thomas Haynes Bayly was born in 1797 and died in 1839. No historical background was found on Bayly, but his musical contribution is significant. Although he may be an obscure composer, his melodies are well-known.

William Duncombe

(done´-comb)

No historical background was found on Duncombe, but his musical contribution is significant. Although he may be an obscure composer, his melodies are well-known.

Franz Joseph Haydn

(high´-den)

Franz Joseph Haydn was born in lower Austria on March 31, 1732, and died on May 31, 1809, in Vienna. When he was five he began to study music. By the age of thirteen he was writing music for the local churches. He wrote vast amounts of music. Each work is full of delights and surprises. Haydn became friends with Mozart. He also accepted Beethoven as a pupil.

Johann Strauss II

(strous)

Johann Strauss II was born in Vienna, Austria on October 25, 1825, and died 1899. He was drawn to music instinctively as a child and began violin lessons at an early age. He not only learned to play the violin, but also to write light music at age six. He made his first appearance conducting his own orchestra at age nineteen. He was known as the "Waltz King."

Giuseppe Verdi

(vair´-dee)

Giuseppe Verdi was born on October 10, 1813, and died January 21, 1901. He was Italy's foremost composer of operas. As a child he showed great interest in all kinds of music-making, whether at church or in the streets. His father bought a spinet which became his favorite instrument. His music was appreciated by many musicians, including J.S. Bach.

Lyrics

Happy Jack

Long Long Ago

Thomas Haynes Bayly (1797-1839)

I have a dog, Happy Jack is his name,
How could he be, so hard to train?
Must have a wire shorting out in his brain,
My little dog, Happy Jack.

Chorus
Tell him to fetch, Happy Jack wants to stay,
Tell him to sit, Happy Jack runs away,
When will my dog ever learn to obey?
My little dog, Happy Jack.

Told Happy Jack "stay away from the trash!"
Then in the night, heard such a crash,
Out from the pile he arose in a flash,
My little dog, Happy Jack.
(chorus)

Told Happy Jack "see a cat, let her be!"
There Happy sat, smiling at me,
Next day he chased twenty cats up a tree,
My little dog, Happy Jack.

Took Happy Jack to obedience school,
That's where he learned every rule,
Now people think that my doggie is cool,
My little dog, Happy Jack.

Chorus
Now he can fetch,
Shake a paw and play dead,
Roll over twice, even stand on his head,
Turns out the lights, even makes his own bed,
My little dog, Happy Jack.

Chorus
Here is a lesson for you and for me,
It's good advice and I hope you agree,
We need to live more obediently,
Just like my dog, Happy Jack,
Just like my dog, Happy Jack,
My little dog, Happy Jack.

In One Ear and Out the Other

Anvil Chorus from *Il Trovatore*

Giuseppe Verdi

My mother told me to take off my rain boots,
Before I come through the kitchen door,
Next thing I know down the hallway I go,
With a trail of mud right across the floor,
Why don't I listen?
Before it's too late?

Chorus
Things go inside one ear and then right out the other,
Why is it always hard to listen to my mother?
She knows what's best, obedience.
She makes it so clear, it goes in one ear and out the other.

My mother told me to put on my jacket,
I run out the door saying I'll be fine,
Next thing I know I'm in bed with a cold,
Runny nose and a fever of ninety-nine,
Why don't I listen?
Before it's too late?

My mother told me to do all my homework,
Before I go out with my friends to play,
Next thing I know is I have to stay home,
And do all of my homework on Saturday,
Why don't I listen?
Before it's too late?

Last Chorus
Things go inside one ear, don't let them out the other,
Let's try obedience, and listen to your mother,
She knows what's best, obedience,
She makes it so clear, it goes in one ear, not out the other.

Little Willy, Will He?

Gypsy Rondo from *Trio in G*

Joseph Haydn

Little Willy, Little Willy, he would not obey,
And he would not follow all the rules when he would play.
Oh, he pushed and shoved and shoved and pushed
And pushed and shoved and shoved and pushed and
No one liked to play with Little Willy, Little Will.

Little Willy, Little Willy, he would not obey,
And he would not do as he was told,
"I want my way!"
Oh, he disobeyed, "I want my way!"
He disobeyed, "I want my way!"
And no one liked to play with Little Willy,
Little Will.

Little Willy
Will he, will he
Learn to obey
When he's at play?
Little Will, if you want to obey,
Then others will want to play
With you, it's true.
Oh yes, it's true,
It's true, it's very true!

And if you'll follow all the rules at school,
And not insist you get your way,
Then you will find you'll have good times,
Obey!
Obey, obey, obey, oh.

Little Willy, Little Will
He now obeys!
"Such a wonderful, delightful boy,"
Others will say!
Little Will, it's such a thrill,
He now obeys whene'er he plays!
Oh, Little Will, you now obey
And yes, with you we want to play!

Oh, Little Will, we want to play with you,
We want to play with you, obey!

Obey, Don't Stray

Tales from the Vienna Woods

Johann Strauss II

"Stay in the yard;
Don't stray away,"
Said Little Tim to Pup one day.
But Pup would not
Obey Tim's words,
And wandered off to see the world.
Around the corner,
Came a van,
A dog catcher, with net in hand.
"Oh, no!" said Pup, "I'm doomed!

"I disobeyed and woe is me,
Disobeyed and now I see;
I'm so upset!
Here comes the net!
Better run to my yard,
Obedience is not that hard,
When you see a dog catcher's net start to fall on your head!"

Obey, Obey
I will obey
Stay in the yard,
I will not stray,
I'll follow Tim's
Advice for me,
Stay in the yard, I'll not run free.

"Stay in the yard;
Don't stray away.
I hope you've learned
How to obey."

"I learned my lesson, yes, sir-ee!
Learned the lesson to stay free!
I'm safe today
I now obey
Little Tim, I'll be like you,
Do the things you tell me to,
Little Pup will not stray,
I have learned to obey."

Stop, Look at the Sign!

Sonatina in C Major

William Duncombe

Chorus
Stop, look at the sign,
Do what it says because it's there to help you,
Stop, make up your mind,
Study it close, obey the sign!
Stop, look at the sign,
Giving important information to you,
Stop, make up your mind,
Do what it says, obey the sign.

"Warning," "Caution," "Stay Away,"
"Don't Feed the Animals Today,"
These are the signs, we will obey them,
Everywhere we go. *(chorus)*

"Wait" and "Yield," "Stop" and "Go"
There's "Walk" and "Don't Walk," "Fast" and "Slow" and
"Right Turn," "Left Turn,"
"Open," "Closed,"
To help the traffic flow—so,
(chorus)

Every sign is for a reason,
"Danger," "Keep Out," "Hunting Season"
"No Trespassing" on a tree then,
Go back where you came from.
(chorus)

By the lake it says "Thin Ice"
"Beware of Dog" is good advice,
Obey the sign, or pay the price,
Now you know what to do—so,
(chorus)

Stop, because it's there to help you,
Stop, obey the sign,
Stop, important information to you,
Stop, it says obey the sign.

Word Search

Find and circle all of the words in the puzzle below. The words are listed below the puzzle. The words may read across, down, backwards, or diagonally. The first one has been circled for you.

Y	D	B	H	K	R	S	F	O	L	L	O	W	G	X	F	Z
A	I	N	S	T	R	U	C	T	I	O	N	S	H	M	U	Y
G	R	E	I	O	J	B	L	J	P	R	A	A	D	R	L	I
C	E	F	L	R	Q	M	N	E	Q	T	E	R	N	O	F	B
A	C	E	N	D	E	I	R	L	S	N	H	S	E	F	I	Y
U	T	L	M	E	O	S	Y	E	B	O	Q	R	P	R	L	M
T	I	T	P	R	M	S	L	H	K	C	G	A	E	E	L	C
H	O	Q	E	S	G	I	C	T	I	J	T	S	D	P	C	E
O	N	R	V	N	U	O	B	E	D	I	E	N	C	E	D	T
R	S	W	Y	A	D	N	R	E	S	P	O	N	D	N	P	X
I	C	O	M	P	L	I	A	N	T	E	B	V	F	S	J	O
T	X	A	G	R	E	E	A	B	L	E	U	T	U	L	V	C
Y	B	F	S	D	Z	S	U	R	R	E	N	D	E	R	W	K

✓1. AGREEABLE
2. ATTEND
3. AUTHORITY
4. COMPLIANT
5. CONTROL
6. DEPEND
7. DIRECTIONS
8. FOLLOW
9. FULFILL
10. INSTRUCTIONS
11. OBEDIENCE
12. OBEY
13. ORDERS
14. PERFORM
15. RESPECT
16. RESPOND
17. RULES
18. SUBMISSION
19. SURRENDER
20. YIELD

Find the Words

Work the puzzle by writing the name of the pictures in the blanks. Then copy the numbered letters into the correct blanks below. Make sure you are obedient by following these directions!

___ ___ ___ ___
1 2 3 4

___ ___ ___ ___ ___ ___ ___
5 6 7

___ ___ ___ ___ ___ ___ ___ ___ ___
8 9 10

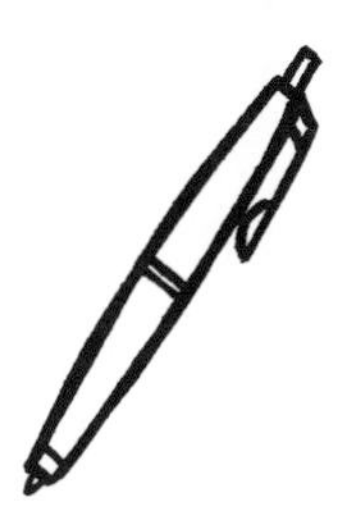

___ ___ ___
11 12

Write your message here:

___ ___ ___ ___   ___ ___ ___ ___
2 1 5 10   10 2 8 9

___ ___ ___ ___ ___ ___ ___
11 3 9 5 12 4 7

Mystery Message

What happens when you obey? Find the answer in the puzzle below. With a dark crayon, color out every X and Z. The remaining letters will tell you the mystery message.

X	Y	Z	O	Z	Z	X	U
F	X	X	Z	E	Z	E	Z
Z	L	X	X	Z	G	Z	O
Z	Z	O	X	D	X	X	I
N	X	Z	S	X	Z	I	Z
Z	Z	D	X	X	E	Z	X

Going from left to right, copy the remaining letters on the blanks below to reveal the mystery message.

___ ___ ___   ___ ___ ___ ___

___ ___ ___ ___   ___ ___ ___ ___ ___ ___

There are times when obedience is difficult, but you still feel good inside. Can you think of some times that you obeyed? List them below and tell how you felt.

1.____

2.____

3.____

Code Buster

There is a special kind of obedience that makes parents and teachers happy. Find out what kind of obedience this is by breaking the code below.

Match the letters under the blanks with a letter in the code box. Write the correct letter in the blanks.

___ ___ ___ ___ ___ ___ ___ ___ ___
L Y V W R V M X V

___ ___ ___ ___ ___ ___   ___ ___
H S L F O W   Y V

___ ___ ___ ___ ___ ___
K I L N K G

___ ___ ___
Z M W

___ ___ ___ ___ ___ ___ ___ ___!
X S V V I U F O

What kind of obedience makes parents or teachers unhappy?

1.____

2.____

3.____

Find the Letter

There is something you should have when you obey your parents, teacher, or those in authority. If you have this, it will make everyone happy!

Follow the instructions and write the correct letter in the box.

I'm a letter in FLAG, but not in FLAT ☐

I'm a letter in BOY, but not in BAY ☐

I'm a letter in SOLO, but not in SILO ☐

I'm a letter in DAY, but not in SAY ☐

I'm a letter in SAME, but not in SOME ☐

I'm a letter in BAT, but not in BAG ☐

I'm a letter in TAKE, but not in CAKE ☐

I'm a letter in RIPE, but not in ROPE ☐

I'm a letter in SAT, but not in SAW ☐

I'm a letter in RUG, but not in RAG ☐

I'm a letter in LEAD, but not in LEAF ☐

I'm a letter in EAT, but not in SAT ☐

I should have a __ __ __ __ __ __ __ __ __ __ __ __

when I am asked to do something.

Patience
pa'·tience
Calmly overcoming and enduring troubles, delays, and problems without complaining.
"All things come round to him who will but wait."
-Longfellow

Composers

The following composers' melodies were used for the Patience songs.

Johann Sebastian Bach (bock)

Johann Sebastian Bach was born in Germany on March 21, 1685, and died July 28, 1750. He was one of the greatest and most productive geniuses in the history of Western music. He received his first musical instruction from his father, a town musician. When he was ten, his father died. He went to live and study with his older brother who taught him to play the clavichord. When he was only fifteen he began to earn his own living as a chorister at the Church of St. Michael in Luneburg. He is recognized as one of the greatest composers that ever lived and some call him the "Father of Music."

Edvard Grieg (greeg)

Edvard Grieg was born in Bergen, Norway on June 15, 1843, and died September 4, 1907. He was Norway's greatest composer and founded a national school of Norwegian music. His mother began teaching him piano when he was six years old.

Aram Khachaturian **(catch´-a-tour´-ee-on)**

Aram Khachaturian was born in Tbilisi, Russia in 1903 and died in 1978. He was a composer educated at the Moscow Conservatory. In 1959 he was awarded the Lenin Prize. He wrote Armenian folk music as well as symphonies. His music is colorful and has continued the nationalist tradition.

Felix Mendelssohn **(men´-dull-son)**

Felix Mendelssohn was born in Hamburg, Germany on February 3, 1809, and died in Leipzig on November 4, 1847. When French troops occupied Hamburg in 1811, his family moved to Berlin. There little Felix, age three, began to study the piano with his mother. When he was nine, he made his first public appearance as a pianist. At age eleven he performed his first original compositions. He was a genius in his writing, playing, and knowledge. He was very generous to other musicians.

Wolfgang Amadeus Mozart **(moats´-art)**

Wolfgang Amadeus Mozart was born in Salzburg, Austria, on January 27, 1756 with the name Johannes Chrysostomus Wolfgangus Theophilus Mozart and died in Vienna on December 5, 1791. He began to play the piano when he was three years old. By the age of six he had become an accomplished performer on the clavier, violin, and organ and was highly skilled in sight-reading and improvisation. He is considered by some to be the greatest musical genius of all time.

Lyrics

All Grown Up!

Sleeper, Wake

Johann Sebastian Bach

Chorus
I'm tired of being just a kid,
I wanna be big, all grown up,
It really can't happen soon enough,
I wanna be big, all grown up!

Verse1

'Cause then I could stay up late and watch TV,
I could even eat most anything I wanted,
A grown-up can drive a car,
And be where big people are,
I wouldn't have any school,
I'd get to be in charge,
And even make all the rules,
have cash and credit cards,
I hope you see that what I want to be is all grown up.

Chorus 2
We're tired of being just a kid,
We wanna be big, all grown up,
It really can't happen soon enough,
We wanna be big, all grown up!

Chorus 3
Be patient and glad to be a kid,
One day you'll be big, all grown up,
It really will happen soon enough,
One day you'll be big, all grown up.

Remember that being young is not so bad,
Being grown up has a certain disadvantage,
You go to work every day,
No cartoons on Saturday,
You have to wear funny clothes, no time for make-believe,
Or playing catch, you've got those responsibilities,
So have some fun, be a kid, your day will come
to be grown up.

Be patient, it may be slow,
But each day you will see you grow,
Don't be in a hurry,
Just decide to be a kid and enjoy the time.

© 1997 Angel Creek Music

Are We There Yet?

Symphony No. 40 in G Minor
Molto Allegro Movement

Wolfgang Amadeus Mozart

Are we there, are we there, are we there yet?
We're the kids in the back of the car.

Are we there, are we there, are we there yet?
We've been driving and driving so far,
It's taking us forever,
Please tell us how much longer, are we gonna
be there soon?
How soon? Real soon? Why not? Aren't we there yet?

Are we there, are we there, are we there yet?
We don't know how much more we can take.
Are we there, are we there, are we there yet?
We don't know how much longer.
Can we stop somewhere, anywhere,
We passed a perfect place back there,
Please, get us out of here right now!
Are we there yet, are we there yet?

Chorus
Children, children, have you heard of patience?
We still have another hour to go,
Here's your chance to show a little patience,
Sit there quietly and stop complaining, try restraining,
Settle down and wait!
Please cooperate and demonstrate that you can wait,
And everyone will feel much better when you do.
Patience, patience,
Are we there, are we there, are we there?
Patience helps you through.
Are we there, are we there, are we there?
It's good for you!

Are we there, are we there, are we there yet?
Can we stop and get something to eat?
Are we there, are we there, are we there yet?
We just need to get out of our seat!
We're thirsty and we're tired,
We have to use the bathroom, are we gonna be there soon?
How soon? Real soon? Why not? Aren't we there yet?

Are we there, are we there, are we there yet?
We're so bored, we don't know what to do,
Are we there, are we there, are we there yet?
We are tired of the same old view!
Let's stop somewhere, anywhere,
We passed the perfect place back there,
Please get us out of here right now!
Are we there yet, are we there yet?

Are we there yet?
We're not there yet, please don't forget!
It's good for you, patience will get you through!

© 1997 Angel Creek Music

Don't Be So Impatient!

Spring Song

Felix Mendelssohn

Chorus
Don't be so impatient when you have to wait,
Don't kick and scream or make a scene,
For soon it will be over,
One day somebody else will have to wait for you,
But now it's still your turn,
Don't be impatient!

Your sister's in the bathroom,
And you need to get in real soon,
You've got hair and teeth to brush,
You're really in a rush,
Stop knocking on the door,
And pounding on the floor,
'Cause no matter what, there's
one important fact you can't ignore,
Your turn will come and soon you won't be waiting anymore!

Your mama's in the kitchen,
And you're waiting for your dinner,
You're as hungry as a horse,
Now where is that main course?
Don't holler and complain,
It only hurts your brain,
And no matter what, there's one important fact you can't ignore,
Your food will come and soon you won't be waiting anymore!

You're standing on the corner,
And you're waiting for the bus,
It's so cold and wet outside,
And you don't see the ride,
Don't kick and stomp your feet,
Be calm and take a seat,
'Cause no matter what, there's one important fact you can't ignore,
The bus will come and soon you won't be waiting anymore!

© 1997 Angel Creek Music

I Want It Now!

Sabre Dance

Aram Khachaturian

Heard my alarm clock warning,
Got right out of bed this morning,
Brushed my teeth and combed my hair,
Put on my clothes, ran down the stairs,
Where is my breakfast,
Quick, I want it now!
Patience, patience.
There's porridge in the pot,
But now I want it steaming hot,
I throw it in the microwave,
I can't believe the time I save,
Where is my coat? I have to have it now!
Patience, patience.

I scurry out the door,
I've never been so late before,
Hop on the bus, the traffic's bad,
I start to fuss, I'm getting mad,
I've got to make it there on time somehow! Patience, patience.
Everyone is in my way,
It happens to me everyday
No time to talk I've got to run,
There's so much work left to be done,
I need a few more hours in my day!
Patience, patience.

Chorus
People rushing by, on the fly, you and I,
wonder why,
Need to slow it down, look around, get our feet on the ground,
We want patience and we want it now!

Down at the shopping mall,
Grab this and that, I want it all,
I've got to be the first in line,
Just ring me up, I don't have time,
There's something else I've got to do right now!
Patience, patience.
Drive through the laundromat,
I get it done in seconds flat,
And then the hour photo place
The grocery store at hectic pace,
I need some milk and eggs, I want them now! Patience, patience.

When dinner's what I want,
I find a fast food restaurant,
A hamburger, a fries, and coke,
An apple pie, come on, slowpoke,
Hey, can you hurry up? I want it now!
Patience, patience.
Once dinner's in my sight,
I eat it in a single bite,
Rush out the door, I'm running late,
There's never time to hesitate,
There's somewhere else I have to be right now!
Patience, patience.

Chorus
People rushing by, on the fly, you and I,
wonder why,
Need to slow it down, look around, get our feet on the ground,
We want patience and we want it now!

© 1997 Angel Creek Music

Turtle Joe

Norwegian Dance Op. 35, No. 2

Edvard Grieg

I'm turtle Joe,
And I'm so slow,
I'm moving fast as any turtle can go,
Everybody seems to just pass me by,
Doesn't seem to matter how hard I try.

Will you be my friend,
Or are you always in a hurry?
Have you any patience,
Will you wait for me?

He's turtle Joe
And he's so slow,
He's moving fast as any turtle can go,
Everybody seems to just pass him by,
Doesn't seem to matter how hard he tries,

We will be your friends,
And we're not always in a hurry,
We have lots of patience,
We will wait for you.

Here come chipmunks, hopping past, real fast,
We are in a hurry,
Never any time to waste,
We're always in a flurry,
We can't wait for you!
Here and there we scurry
Slowing down is never good,
'Cause then we'll start to worry,
We've got things to do!
Humming birds are flying by, way up high,
We are in a hurry,
We can't even wait a minute,
Always in a flurry,
Look out we're coming through!
Through the air we scurry,
Nature is depending on us,
We don't have the time to wait for you!

I'm turtle Joe,
And I'm so slow,
I'm moving fast as any turtle can go,
Everybody seems to just pass me by,
Doesn't seem to matter how hard I try,
When you find a friend who,
Always patient waiting for you,
Then you know you've found a
Friend who will be true!

He's turtle Joe,
And he's so slow,
He's moving fast as any turtle can go,
Everybody seems to just pass him by,
Doesn't seem to matter how hard he tries,
We will be your friends who,
Always will be waiting for you,
We have lots of patience,
We'll wait for you.

© 1997 Angel Creek Music

Patience Puzzler

Your mother promises to take you somplace that is very special. But first, she has to finish her work. It is very hard for you to wait. What should you do if you want to be a patient person?

To find the answer, make a word that means the opposite of the first word. Then copy the circled letters in the numbered spaces below.

1. OPEN — C (18) ___ ___ (6)
2. BIG — L (8) ___ (22) ___ (1)
3. START — F ___ (2) ___ ___ (10)
4. IN — O (11) (4) (9)
5. GO — C (14) ___ (16) ___
6. CLOUDY — C ___ ___ (19) (5)
7. END — B ___ ___ (20) (21)
8. CRY — L ___ (12) ___ ___
9. UP — D (3) ___ (7) ___
10. BOTTOM — T (13) (15) ___ 17

___ ___ ___ ___ ___ ___   ___ ___ ___ ___ ___ ___ ___
1 2 3 4 5 6   7 8 9 10 11 12 13

___ ___ ___ ___ ___ ___ ___ ___ ___
14 15 16 17 18 19 20 21 22

Patience Maze

Can you be patient and find your way through the maze from start to finish?

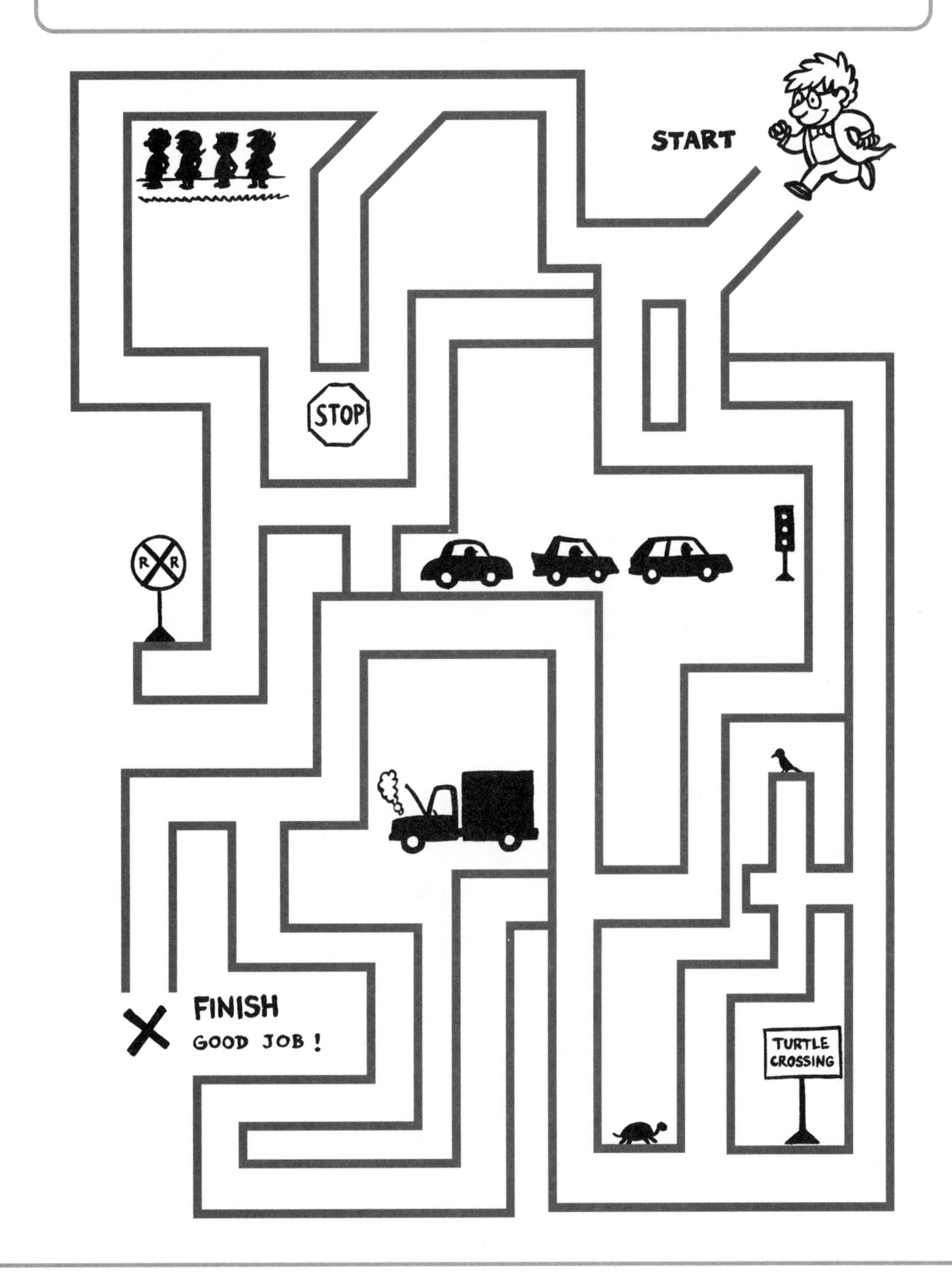

Crossword Puzzle

Use the words from the word box to finish the sentences. Then use the same words to complete the puzzle.

complain	joy	pushing	save	wait
endurance	patient	reward	swimming	yell

ACROSS

2. I will _____________ my turn.
4. A long car trip takes a lot of patient _____________ .
5. I must be _____________ when things don't go as I planned.
7. Be patient and don't go _____________ right after lunch.
9. I will not _____________ when Mother says I will have to wait for her.

DOWN

1. Patience will reap a _____________ .
3. I will _____________ my money and wait until I have enough to buy a bicycle.
5. _____________ and shoving shows impatience.
6. If my brother breaks my toy, I will show patience and not _____________ at him.
8. A patient person is a _____________ to be around.

1. 2. 3. 4. 5. 6. 7. 8. 9.

Fishing for Patience

Fishing takes a lot of patience! Decide which hooks will catch the Patience Fish. Then write the words on the fish and color it.

Who Is Showing Patience?

Who is showing patience in the pictures below? Read what each person is saying in the first picture. Then write what you think they are saying in the second picture. Circle whether you think the person is patient or impatient.

"This math problem takes too long." ""

Patient or impatient

Patient or impatient

"I can't put this model airplane together." ""

Patient or impatient

Patient or impatient

"I want these cookies now!" ""

Patient or impatient

Patient or impatient

Perseverance

per' · se · ver' · ance

Not giving up, but staying with any task, job, or purpose until it is completed.

"Perseverance is not a long race; it is many short races, one after the other."

-Walter Elliot

Composers

The following composers' melodies were used for the Perseverance songs.

Johannes Brahms

(broms)

Johannes was born in Hamburg, Germany, on the 7th of May, 1833, and died the 3rd of April, 1897. He studied with his father, who was a double bassist in the Hamburg Theatre. By the age of 14, he was playing his own compositions in public. He is best remembered for his open mindedness and great enthusiasm. Brahms was a greatly admired composer, even by those who opposed his style of music. Today he is considered one of the world's greatest composers.

Edvard Grieg

(greeg)

Edvard was born in Norway on June 15, 1843, and died there on September 4, 1907. His mother began to give him piano lessons when he was 6 years old. At the age of 15, he entered the Leipzig Conservatory of Music and graduated with honors. The rhythms and melodies of Norwegian folk music were the base of his music and he became Norway's greatest composer.

Franz Liszt

(list)

Franz was born in Hungary on October 22, 1811. He died on July 31, 1886. He was often considered one the world's greatest pianists, as well as an outstanding composer. Even his worst compositions were liked. He was instructed as a boy by his father, an amateur musician, and gave his first concert at the age of 9 for the prince. The prince was so impressed, he paid for Liszt's education for the next six years. Liszt went to Vienna to study. He is considered to be among the greatest pianists there has ever been.

Robert Schumann

(shoe´-mon)

Robert was born in Germany on June 8, 1810, and died on July 29, 1856. He was born to a wealthy book seller and inherited a love of romantic poetry. When he was 14, he published some verses. His mother wanted him to study law, but his music teacher persuaded her to let him study music. Robert wanted to become a great pianist, but a crippled finger turned him to composition. He was one of the greatest composers for the pianoforte and was a big influence on the music of his time.

Peter Tchaikovsky

(chy-cough´-ski)

Peter Tchaikovsky, whose name can also be spelled Tschaikowsky, was born on May 7, 1840, and died November 6, 1893 in Russia. He wrote some of the most beautiful music ever written. A favorite is the *Nutcracker* ballet. He wrote the music to a story by Hoffman.

Emil Waldteufel

(val-toe-fell)

Emil was born in the town of Strasbourg on December 9, 1837, and died in Paris on February 16, 1915. At a young age he became a student at the Paris Music Conservatory. Later in life he became the court pianist and the director of court balls for the Empress Eugenie. He is known especially for his waltzes.

Lyrics

Little Sparrows

The Nutcracker Suite
Dance of the Reed Flutes
Peter Tchaikovsky

Hear the sounds of earth,
there's singing;
Tiny sparrows perched upon their nests.
On this day of spring,
Spread their tiny wings,
Now it's time to try,
fly, try to fly high.

Flutter, flitting,
flapping feathers,
Tiny wings it's time to give your best,
Flap your little wings,
On this day of spring,
Now it's time to fly,
Time to fly.

From the nest the tiny sparrows take their step
And soon discover
that the time is now
To reach the heights
and search the skies.

One by one they stretch their wings
and lift their heads
and start to sing
The moment they've been waiting for,
the test now has arrived.

Suddenly into the air the sparrows
start to falter, sputter,
Then they fan the breeze
with greater strength
and start to fly.

Up and down they tumble, tumble.
Will they falter, will they stumble?
Will they fall to earth
Or will they soar into the sky
And start to fly, and start to fly,
and start to fly to the sky?

Flying high above the rooftops,
Soaring in the sky among the clouds,
Little ones you did it!
Never once did you quit!
Now it's time to fly high,
fly high into the sky!

Take a lesson from the sparrows,
Try your best
and soon you will discover,
That you can do great things,
You'll fly high with strong wings,
Fly so high! Fly so high!

I Won't Give Up!

The Skater's Waltz
Emil Waldteufel

I'm learning to skate
Left foot then right
I'm trying, I'm colliding
I'm such an awkward sight!

I take one small step,
Now I try it twice,
I'm gliding! No colliding!
Across the frozen ice.

At first I fall and then I stand and
Then I fall and try again to glide
'cross the lake.
I'm whirling, twirling, slipping,
Trying oh so hard my head not to break!

I won't give up, I won't give in
I'll try and try and try again
To slide over, try over to glide 'cross the ice.

I'm learning to skate
two, three, one, two, three
Left foot and then right
two, three, one, two
I'm trying, I'm gliding
Now I'm such a graceful sight!

Try, Try Again!

Soldiers' March
Robert Schumann

Don't give up, don't quit, don't stop, don't end
If you do, you might not start again.
Move ahead, press on,
march straight, march strong!
And you'll find you will move right along!

Keep your goal in sight
Try, try again
Be a valiant knight
And you will win.

Don't give up, don't quit, don't stop, don't end
Always try and try and you'll win!
Try with all your might
Give it your best
When you end the race, then you can rest.

You Can Do It!

Hungarian Dance No. 5
Johannes Brahms

The team's behind, the game's near end
You're up to bat, will you strike out again?
The ball is thrown hard, it's sizzling in
And you want to run away,
you wish it were another day
And someone else was at the plate.
Strike!

"Oh, no," you say, "strike one, not again!"
Here comes the pitch, it's curving around the bend.
You grip the bat, you swing with great power
But you miss the ball,
it smacks the catcher's mitt
And once again you hear the umpire yell his call. Strike!

Will you quit, and back off
and kick the ground?
Or stand there strong, and face,
yet, another round?
Keep your head high,
and don't give an inch to doubt
"You can do it!" are the cheers from the crowd.

The pitcher's set, the wind-up, the toss
If you strike out, the game will be lost.
The throw is the best, a blazing swirl of speed
And you know it's time to swing,
your muscles stretch
Your arms they spring,
you swing hard at the ball.

You stood the test, you came here to play!
You smacked the ball and sent it on its way!
Over the fence, the ball's soaring high!
'Cause you did not back away, you stood your ground,
You made the grade, and now you've won the game!

You did not quit, and back off and kick the ground!
You stood there strong,
and faced, yet, another round!
When the pitch came,
you swung with all your might!
Great! You did it right!
Look! How the ball takes to flight!
That's the ballgame!

Finish Line

Hungarian Rhapsody No. 2
Franz Liszt

The race began, Jack Rabbit ran,
Tom Turtle crawled across the land,
Jack bounced and bopped with such great speed,
He burst ahead into the lead.

But Tom kept moving slowly on,
He knew the race was very long.
"What counts is not who darts out fast,
But who will win the race at last."

The race is to the slow but sure,
And from the path do not detour.
Take one small step, move on, endure!
The finish line will soon be yours!

Jack Rabbit flew with such great speed,
That he grew tired and thought that he
Would rest a while beneath a tree,
He knew that he was in the lead.

But Tom moved slowly right ahead,
And with every step he surely said,
"The race is to the slow but sure,
And from the path do not detour!"

When Jack awoke and looked around,
He was surprised by how much ground
He was behind, and not ahead,
And how much Tommy Turtle led.

When Tommy Turtle crossed the line,
Jack Rabbit was still far behind,
"What counts is not who darts out fast
But who will win the race at last!"

The race is to the slow but sure,
And from the path do not detour.
Take one small step, move on, endure!
The finish line will soon be yours!

The Fishing Trip

Peer Gynt Suite
In the Hall of the Mountain King
Edvard Grieg

Jordan got out his fishing pole
Went down to the fishing hole
Like he did the day before
When he brought nothing home.

He had spent all the day
Watching fish get away
On his line they wouldn't stay
And he brought nothing home.

Next day he went back again
With his dog and his best friend
He would bait his hook and then
He'd bring something home.

But again he had bad luck
So he took his dog, Buck,
Back to the house
And he brought nothing home.

He got up the next day
This time he would say
None of them got away
Look what I brought home.

Jordan filled his bucket up
Jordan had lots of luck
He never gave it up
And he brought supper home.

Jordan never gave it up
And he brought supper home!
Jordan never gave it up
And he brought supper home!
If you never give it up
You'll bring supper home!

Number Message

How do you feel when you keep going until the task is finished?

Work the puzzle by writing the name of the object in the squares.

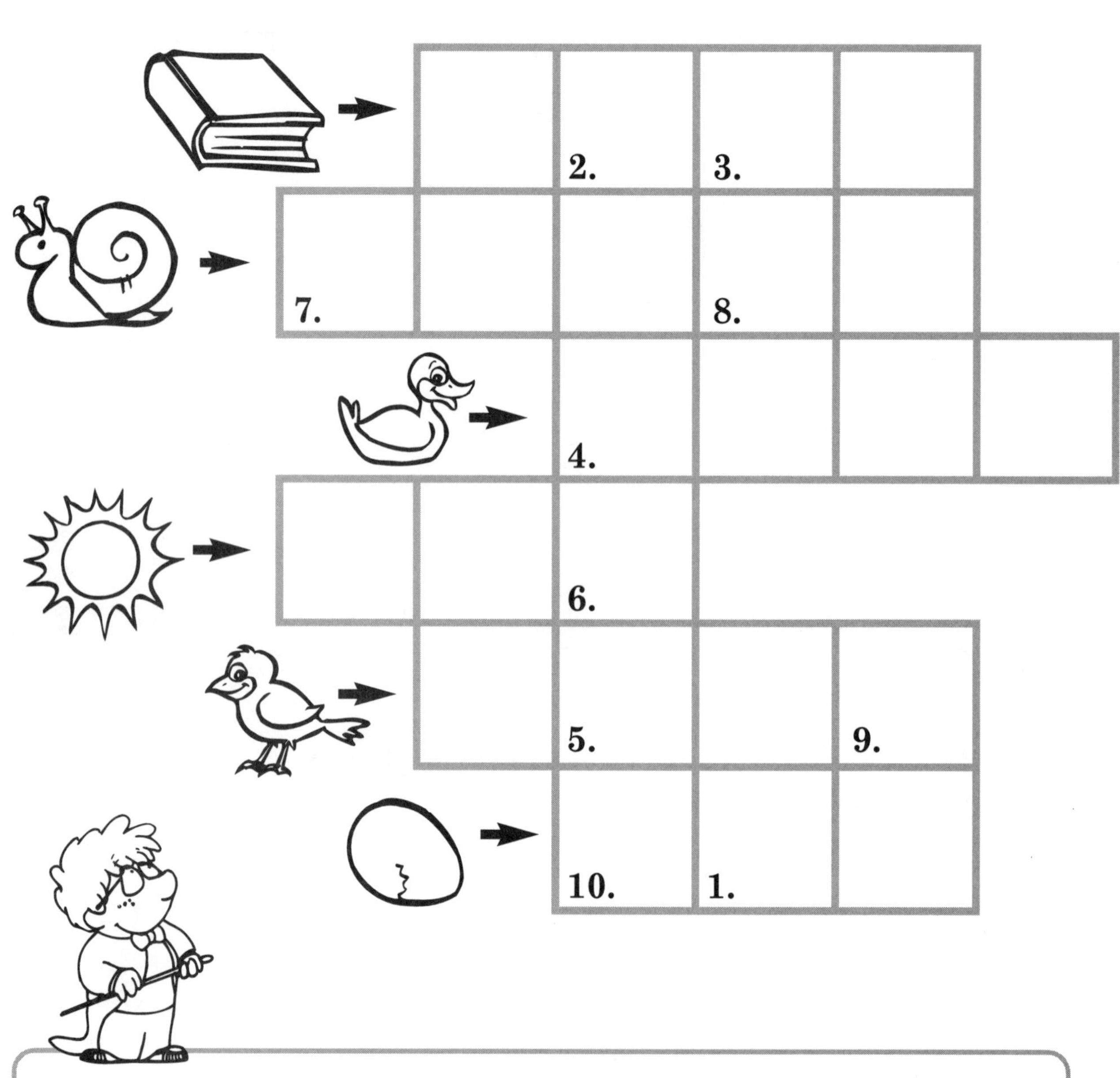

Write the numbered letters in the matching blanks.

____ ____ ____ ____   ____ ____ ____ ____ ____ ____

1 2 3 4   5 6 7 8 9 10

Is this how you feel when your goal is reached?

An Amazing Job

Johnny is trying to find the lost kitten before it gets dark. Can you help him find it? Don't give up.

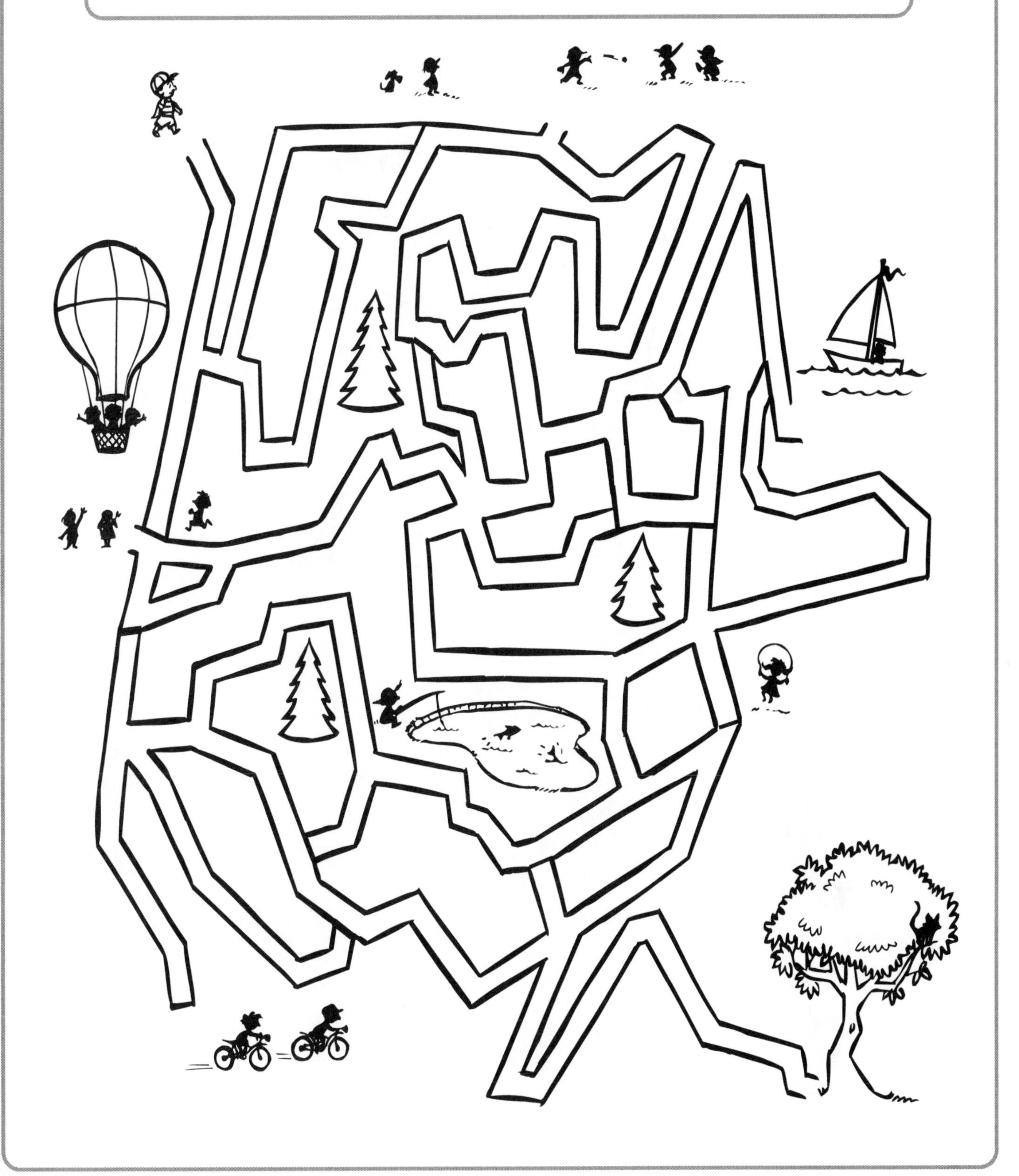

Puzzle Message

Eric's mother lost a pin in the carpet. She asked Eric to look for it. After looking for ten minutes, Eric was ready to quit. His mother gave him this puzzle message. Can you work the puzzle and read the message?

Write the name of the object on the lines.

Copy the numbered letters on the matching numbered blanks.

___ ___ ___ ' ___   ___ ___ ___ ___   ___ ___
6 3 2 1   5 8 4 7   10 9

Practice, Practice

Doing well at some things takes lots of practice. Name these things that need practice. Color the ones you practice regularly.

Draw something else you practice.

Try, Try Again

Josh wants to learn to skateboard. He falls many times, but he keeps trying. Color the picture. Then solve the problems. Match the letters and the answers to the numbers on the lines below. Find out what Josh always says.

"___ ___ ___, ___ ___ ___ ___ ___!"

11 7 12 3   8 4 2 3

N	T	U	W	O	I	L	Q
3 + 9 = __	7 - 4 = __	10 - 6 = __	5 + 6 = __	2 + 5 = __	6 - 4 = __	5 + 4 = __	10 - 2 = __

Respect
re • spect
Showing a courteous consideration, honor, and appreciation for others, their property, and the environment around you.
"He who respects others is respected by them."
-Mencius

Composers

The following composers' melodies were used for the Respect songs.

Engelbert Humperdinck (HOOM per dink)

Engelbert Humperdinck was born in Germany in 1854 and died in 1921. He is famous for two things: writing the classic opera, *Hansel and Gretel*, and lending his name to the well-known popular singer. His parents wanted him to be an architect, but he wanted to study music. He went to Italy in 1879, where he met Wagner and studied with him. He didn't contribute much in the way of composition, but he did have some success with his opera, *Hansel and Gretel*, which he based on the Grimm's fairytale.

Josef Stauss (STROWS)

Josef Strauss was born in Vienna, Austria, in 1827 and died there in 1870. He was the second son of Johann Strauss I. He was an architect, but studied music secretly until he joined the family tradition. He formed his own orchestra and wrote 283 works for it to play. His polkas are played today more than his waltzes.

Johann Strauss II (STROWS)

Johann Strauss II was born in Vienna, Austria, on October 25, 1825, and died there on June 3, 1899. He was the son of another famous Strauss, Johann I, who was considered the "father" of the waltz. Johann II wrote his first waltz at the age of 6 and conducted a very successful orchestral concert when he was only 19 years old. He wrote over 450 works, including waltzes, polkas, and marches, and became known as the "Waltz King."

Peter Tchaikovsky (chy COFF skee)

Peter Tchaikovsky, whose name can also be spelled Tschaikowsky, was born on May 7, 1840, and died November 6, 1893 at the age of 53. He is considered the greatest of all Russian composers and the greatest writer of beautiful melodies that ever lived. He studied to be a lawyer until, at the age of 22, his love for music won, and he enrolled in the St. Petersburg Conservatoire.

Lyrics

Speak Respect

Brother Come and Dance With Me - Hansel & Gretel
Engelbert Humperdinck

Verse 1
Here's a song about your beak,
What you say and how you speak,
Sing along, you will see,
How to speak respectfully,

To your mom and dad at home,
To the person on the phone,
Be polite, say something nice,
Speak respect and don't think twice.

Chorus
Speak respect or close your lip,
Courteous or zip, zip, zip,
Careless words get away,
Careful with the things you say.
Open mouth means open trap,
All they hear is yap, yap, yap,
Now you know, don't neglect,
When you speak- Respect!

Honor and appreciate,
Talking back will aggravate,
Careful what rolls off your tongue,
Disrespect hurts everyone!

Chorus
Speak respect or close your lip,
Courteous or zip, zip, zip,
Careless words get away,
Careful with the things you say.
Open mouth means open trap,
All they hear is yap, yap, yap,
Now you know, don't neglect,
When you speak- Respect!

Verse 2
To your teacher at the school,
To the lifeguard at the pool,
Because their rules keep you safe,
Follow them don't hesitate.

Even to your own best friend,
Choose the words that won't offend,
Ask yourself and answer true,
Would you want that said to you?

Chorus
Speak respect or close your lip,
Courteous or zip, zip, zip,
Careless words get away,
Careful with the things you say.
Open mouth means open trap,
All they hear is yap, yap, yap,
Now you know, don't neglect,
When you speak- Respect!

Honor and appreciate,
Talking back will aggravate,
Careful what rolls off your tongue,
Disrespect hurts everyone!

Chorus
Speak respect or close your lip,
Courteous or zip, zip, zip,
Careless words get away,
Careful with the things you say.
Open mouth means open trap,
All they hear is yap, yap, yap,
Now you know, don't neglect,
When you speak- Respect!

Show Respect

Fireproof Polka Francaise, Op. 269
Josef Strauss

Verse 1
When you go to someone's home
Play with toys, not your own,
Don't just throw them every-where,
Handle them with extra care!
Sitting on the desk you see,
Your sister's diary,
She would want her privacy,
Time to show respect!

Chorus
It's a lesson you should never forget- to show respect!
Being courteous, considerate, you won't regret!
And the more you give the more you will get- so show respect!
When respect is what you do,
Then respect comes back to you,
Respect, respect,

It's time to show respect!

Verse 2
When you see a traffic light,
On the road, shining bright,
Red means stop, you have to wait,
Respect the law, don't hesitate!

If you see an apple tree,
Not on your property
Doesn't mean the apple's free
Time to show respect!

Chorus
It's a lesson you should never forget- to show respect!
Being courteous, considerate, you won't regret!
And the more you give the more you will get- so show respect!
When respect is what you do,
Then respect comes back to you,
Respect, respect,
It's time to show respect!

Verse 3
Show respect in all you do,
Others will respect you,
Let's go out and be our best,
Let's all show respect-OH, YES!

Respect Your Momma and Papa

Hunting, Fast Polka, Op. 373
Johann Strauss, II

Chorus
Respect your momma, respect your papa,
They only tell ya things they oughta,
They're thinking of you, because they love you,
Will you honor, admire, respect?
Respect your momma, respect your papa,
'Cause in the end, they know what's good for you,
Appreciate them, don't aggravate them,
They deserve it, they earned it, respect!

Verse 1
Mother says close your mouth and eat up all your food,
I say, "Yes Ma'am," and I eat up all my food.
Father says do come down from atop the furniture,
I say, "Yes Sir" getting off the furniture!

Chorus
Respect your momma, respect your papa,
They only tell ya things they oughta,

They're thinking of you, because they love you,
Will you honor, admire, respect?
Respect your momma, respect your papa,
'Cause in the end, they know what's good for you,
Appreciate them, don't aggravate them,
They deserve it, they earned it, respect!

Verse 2
Mother says close the door, close it softly, do not slam,
I say "Yes Ma'am," close the door, do not slam.
Father says keep it down,
all that racket will you stop?
I say, "Yes Pop," all the noise I will stop.

Bridge
Do it and don't talk back
No more of your wise cracks,
Then you'll be right on track,
Treat them with respect!
Do what they both request,
Always be on your best,
Let every yes be yes,
Give them your respect!

Respect your momma, respect your papa,
They only tell ya things they oughta,
They're thinking of you, because they love you,
Will you honor, admire, respect?

Verse 3
What they say, I will do,
with respect I will come through,
Mother, Father, what you say I will do,
From now on please expect,
I will show you my respect,
Mother, Father, I will show you respect!

Respect-A-Bull

Swan Lake, Op. 20, Spanish Dance
Peter Tchaikovsky

Verse 1
Respect for the angry bull.
He is powerful.
He is mean and strong
And his horns very long.
He stands like he is the king
of the bull-fight ring
Now he stomps his feet,
Then your eyes they will meet!

Chorus
Respect, respect-a-bull this size.
Respect, you will be very wise.
Listen to me more, would-be matador.
Respect, respect-a-bull like this.
Respect, it is my only wish.
Here's some good advice,
respect will save your life!

Verse 2
You bow to the waiting crowd.
They cheer so loud
But you don't even care,
At the bull you will stare.
He smiles with a silly grin.
What a mess you're in.
As he circles around, you are standing your ground.

Chorus
Respect, respect-a-bull this size.
Respect, you will be very wise.
Listen to me more, would-be matador.
Respect , respect-a-bull like this.
Respect, it is my only wish.
Here's some good advice,
respect will save your life!

Verse 3
A wave with your big red cape,
What a big mistake
Now he gathering speed
It's a bull stampede!
He snorts as he makes a charge
Could he be so large?
Give a yell, "Olé!"
And get out of the way.

Chorus
Respect, respect for you and me.
Let's show respect-ability,
Like the matador,
Respect more and more,
Respect, our job is never done,
Respect, respect for everyone,
Now we realize,
Respect-is good advice!

Ending
Now we realize,
Respect-is good advice!
Now we realize,
Respect-is good advice!

Desmond D. Duck

Swan Lake, Op. 20, Dance of the Swans - IV Allegro Moderato
Peter Tchaikovsky

Verse 1
Desmond D. Ducky waddled into class.
The bell had passed.
Teacher said, "Desmond D. where have you been?"
He answered with a grin--"Oh where do I begin?"
"And my homework I really must admit, my dog ate it!"

Desmond D. Duck, be careful what you say
And now you're gonna pay,
detention every day!

Chorus
Desmond D. waddles around all day saying the things that he shouldn't say with no respect, with no respect.
Why is his beak always quacking back?
When will he stop all of his wise quacks
and show respect, and show respect?

Verse 2
One night Desmond was sitting happily watching TV
His mom said, "Desmond, time to go to bed."
He lifted up his head, and this is what he said,
"Not yet, I'm in the middle of a show,
then I will go."
Now Desmond D. is grounded for a week
You better watch your beak, be careful how you speak.

Chorus
Desmond D. waddles around all day
saying the things that he shouldn't say
with no respect, with no respect.
Why is his beak always quacking back?
When will he stop all of his wise quacks
and show respect, and show respect?

Verse 3
Desmond D. Ducky swimming the canal with all his pals.
Then Desmond quacked and started making fun
He laughed at everyone, but still he wasn't done.
"I know you are, but tell me what am I?" was his reply.
He didn't know the message it would send
It really did offend, and now he has no friends.

Last Chorus
Don't have a Desmond D. Ducky day
Don't say the things that you shouldn't say.
Let's show respect.
Let's show respect.
Don't let your mouth do the talking back.
Let's put a stop to the old wise quacks.
And show respect,
let's show respect.

Let's show respect,
let's show respect.
Let's show respect,
let's show respect.
Respect!

Number Message

How can you show respect for your parents? To find the answer, work the puzzle below. Write the name of the object in the squares.

			13		5	
			11	12	3	
				2	7	
1	4	8	16			
			15		10	
		6		9	14	

Write the numbered letters in the matching blanks below.

___ ___ ___ ___ ___   ___ ___ ___ ___   ___ ___ ___ ___ ___ ___ ___

1 2 3 4 5   6 7 8 9   10 11 12 13 14 15 16

Who Is Showing Respect?

Circle the pictures below that show children who are respectful.

Write a sentence that tells how you would show respect to others.

____

____

Maze for the Answer

Find a secret message in the maze below. Go through the maze of letters. There is only one way through the maze. After you have reached the end, go back and cross off every other letter starting with the letter **A** at the arrow. The remaining letters will be a message just for you.

START HERE

A	R	S	E	A	S	R	O	M	P	B	E	O
A	W	H	F	S	D	P	R	T	M	H	P	Y
L	T	A	I	L	K	H	G	Y	U	M	E	L
S	T	E	S	N	O	E	E	S	J	T	M	W
P	O	I	T	W	C	Y	L	V	B	W	A	O
H	T	E	H	R	P	S	B	N	G	D	G	I
A	T	D	J	F	I	B	F	S	C	S	A	C
F	H	R	W	X	A	K	N	A	T	U	C	L
E	H	P	E	O	R	F	S	K	F	Y	P	J
B	W	C	R	E	D	R	E	P	H	R	N	L
E	Y	T	A	L	W	T	A	S	E	A	E	R
U	N	O	R	Y	K	T	O	C	I	P	A	S

END HERE

Write the secret message below:

_ _ _ _ _ _ _ _   _ _ _ _ _ _ _ _   _ _ _

_ _ _ _   _ _ _ _ _   _ _ _ _ _ _ _ _ _   _ _ _ _.

Word Search

Find and circle the words in the puzzle below. The words may read up, down, across, or diagonal. The first one is circled for you.

Y	T	I	R	G	E	T	N	I	L	P	S	N	E
N	E	C	O	U	R	T	E	O	U	S	O	Q	S
B	L	E	O	H	B	A	C	D	F	I	B	E	T
R	E	S	P	E	C	T	V	O	T	U	E	U	E
N	E	H	U	L	L	Q	I	A	D	U	Y	F	E
F	A	L	E	P	C	A	R	E	O	L	N	Y	M
T	A	A	R	E	A	E	N	Y	Z	U	O	P	U
V	D	B	F	M	D	I	K	B	R	F	Y	P	E
Z	C	R	Q	I	C	N	A	T	X	C	H	T	T
I	W	O	S	P	A	D	U	W	A	O	F	O	I
L	E	N	C	H	M	R	B	V	L	I	F	H	L
E	O	O	T	I	E	U	I	D	G	L	D	M	O
C	L	H	R	Z	E	R	E	G	A	R	D	O	P
O	Z	E	A	P	P	R	E	C	I	A	T	E	A

1. ~~ADMIRE~~
2. APPRECIATE
3. CARE
4. CONSIDERATION
5. COURTEOUS
6. ESTEEM
7. GIFT
8. HEED
9. HELP
10. HONOR
11. INTEGRITY
12. NURTURE
13. OBEY
14. POLITE
15. PRIVACY
16. REGARD
17. RESPECT
18. THANK YOU
19. UPHOLD
20. VALUE

Choose Respect

You can show respect by what you say or do. Look at the pictures below. Complete the pictures by writing how you would respond to each situation.

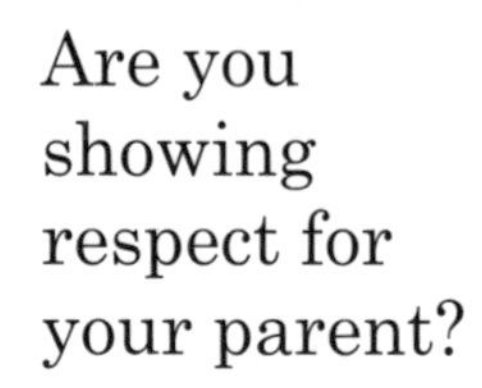

Are you showing respect for your parent?

yes   no

Are you showing respect for the shoppers?

yes   no

Are you showing respect for another's property?

yes   no

Are you showing respect for the environment?

yes   no

Self-Control

self' con·trol'

Bringing my thoughts, words, and actions under control.

"A fool gives vent to all his feelings, but a wise man keeps himself under control."

-Proverbs

Composers

The following composers' melodies were used for the Self-Control songs.

Gioacchino Antonio Rossini (roh SEE nee)

Rossini was born in Pesaro, Italy, February 29, 1792, and died near Paris, France, in 1868. He was probably the most popular and most influential Italian composer during the first half of the 1800's. His father was a trumpeter who played in the local theater. His mother had a beautiful, natural voice. Rossini inherited his father's love for jokes and humour. He inherited his mother's good looks. While he was learning to be a blacksmith, Rossini studied music at school. He decided to become a composer instead and went to a music school in Bologna when he was 14. His first work was produced in 1810. He is best known for his comic operas. His most famous opera is *William Tell.*

Anton Gregor Rubinstein (ROO ben stine)

Rubinstein was born near Balta, Ukraine in 1829 and died in 1894. He was a great Russian pianist and composer. His first teacher was his mother. He made his first appearance when he was 10. When he was 16 he began to teach in Vienna. He was the most famous pianist of his time. He composed many works, but few are performed today. He is best remembered for his *Melody in F.*

Robert Schumann (SHOO mawn)

Schumann was born in Zwickau, Germany in 1810, and died in 1856. Some consider him to be the most important composer of the German romantic period. Schumann is known for his outstanding piano compositions and his beautiful songs. He was the son of a book-seller and publisher and began to take piano lessons when he was around the age of 7.

Johann Strauss, Jr. (strows)

Strauss was born in Vienna on October 25, 1825, and died there on June 3, 1899. He was the son of another famous Strauss (Johann, Sr.), who was considered the "father" of the waltz. Johann, Jr. wrote his first waltz at the age of 6 and conducted a very successful orchestral concert when he was only 19 years old. He was known as the "Waltz King."

Franz von Suppe (ZOO-pay)

Suppe' was born in Dalmatia on April 18, 1819, and died in Vienna on May 21, 1895. He was an Austrian composer of Belgian descent. Suppe' showed musical talent at an early age and wrote his first music at the age of 13. He became the first master of the classical Viennese operetta. He is best known today for his overtures, including *Light Cavalry.*

Lyrics

Self-Control To The Rescue

William Tell Overture
Gioacchino Rossini

Verse 1
If you fall in the mud on a rainy day,
Or your friend down the road won't come out to play,
And you're not gonna stop 'til you get your way,
To the rescue it is self-control.
If they call you a name and it makes you mad,
Get a bump on your head and it hurts so bad,
If your sister breaks every toy you had,
To the rescue it is self-control.
Chorus 1
Self-control will be there to defend you
from a possible catastrophe,
When you're angry and mad, if you have some
self-control there's no emergency,
Stay cool, very calm and collected when things
don't go quite the way you planned,
It'll turn out okay as long as self-control is in
command!
One thing we all need is more self-control,
Let's take it with us wherever we go! HEY!
Verse 2
When it's candy you want, but your mom says no,
There's a party and you're not allowed to go,
If you walk in the dark and you stub your toe,
To the rescue it is self-control.
Someone takes the remote when you watch TV,
If you got only two, but your friend got three,
If you fall off a bike and skin your knee,
To the rescue it is self-control.
Chorus 2
Self-control has come to save the day,
So round up your emotions and don't let them
get away,
Self-control, you know just what to do,
Make sure all of that anger doesn't get the best of you!
Verse 3
When you're trying to rush, others take their time,
And there's something you need, but you're last in line,
Found a hole in your pants and you lost your dime,
To the rescue it is self-control.
If you're playing a game and it seems unfair,
Someone else sits down in your favorite chair,
What your brother has he will never share,
To the rescue it is self-control.
Chorus 1
Verse 4
When your Dad says, "Time to go to bed,"
When your friends pick somebody else instead,
And if nobody hears a word you said,
To the rescue it is self-control.
When your mom gives you one more job to do,
When you finally arrive but the game's all through,
If you walk and you trip and they laugh at you,
To the rescue it is self-control.
Chorus 2
Chorus 1
Verse 1
Ending
When everything is getting out of hand,
You've gotta relax!
Let self-control be in command,
Because we all need self-control,
More self-control,
And where you go, be sure to show, you're in control,
We all need self-control.

© 1998 Angel Creek Music

Get Yourself Under Control!

Tritsch, Tratsch Polka, Op. 214
Johann Strauss, Jr.

Verse 1
That speeding car you're driving without brakes,
A meteor traveling through outer space,
A train that's gone completely off the tracks,
You lose control, and there's no turning back.
Chorus
And that is why you need self-control, self-control, self-control,
Control yourself everywhere you go,
Get yourself under control!
Don't let things just build and build and build,
If you don't stop it, no one will, it's true!
You know what to do!
Take a breath, close your eyes, let the storm pass you by,
If you don't, you'll end up just like a . . .
Verse 2
. . . Boulder rolling down a mountainside,
A twister spinning, whirling through the sky,
An air-o-plane that's running out of gas,
You lose control, you're headed for a crash!
Bridge
When you want your own way, don't say, "No Way!"
Things will turn out OK,
When you learn to have a little self-control.

Someone makes you angry, real mad, so bad,
Don't blow up, that's so sad,
Pull yourself together, you need self-control.

When you feel you've reached the boiling point, then,
Don't let yourself get all out of joint,
With self-control you're turning down the heat,
Stay cool! You won't get burned!
EEEEOOOOWWWW!

When you've got to have it, don't just grab it,
That's an awful habit,
The only thing you need to have is self-control!
Verse 1
Chorus
Verse 2
Ending
Self-control, self-control,
Get yourself in control, that's self-control.

© 1998 Angel Creek Music

Control Yourself

Joyous Farmer
Robert Schumann

Control your mouth and everything you say,
And talking bad to mom or dad is not OK,
You're telling jokes, and laughing, making fun,
And every careless word you say could hurt someone,
And deep inside, you'll know what's wrong or right!
Control yourself and everything you do,
Just walk away, don't let it take control of you!

Control your ears and everything you hear,
The message on the radio is loud and clear,
And when your friends have nothing good to say,
You say "good-bye," you'll see them on another day,
And deep inside, you'll know what's wrong or right!
Control yourself and everything you do,
Just walk away, don't let it take control of you!

Control your eyes and everything you see,
The books you read, the show you're watching on TV,
The magazines and videos you rent,
And every movie isn't always time well spent,
'Cause deep inside, you'll know what's wrong or right!
Control yourself and everything you do,
Just walk away, don't let it take control of you!
Control yourself, control yourself!

Control your feet and everywhere you go,
A "Keep Out" sign, make up your mind and just say "No!"
The places where you know you shouldn't be,
Do not trespass, stay off the grass, it's clear to me,
And deep inside, you'll now what's wrong or right!
Control yourself and everything you do,
Just walk away, don't let it take control of you!

Control yourself, control yourself!

Control your hands and everything you touch,
Those things that don't belong to you,
you want so much,
And never shove, or push or pull or grab,
Don't hit your brother or your sister when you're
mad,
And deep inside, you'll know what's wrong or right!
Control yourself, and everything you do,
Just walk away, don't let it take control of you!

© 1998 Angel Creek Music

Stop! If You Lose Control

Melody in F
Anton Rubinstein
Chorus

Stop, take a breath if you're out of control,
Try to relax, don't overreact,
'Cause losing your cool never solved any problem,
Stop, if you lose control.

Maurice and his mother went shopping at the
market,
He wanted popcorn, his mother told him, "No,"
So he kicked and he thrashed and he threw
quite a fit,
And boy he looked silly when he finished it!

Pete and Patricia were playing at the playground,
They found a ball that was lying on the grass,
"It's mine!" "No, it's mine!" "No, I found it first!"
They grabbed and they pulled, but that just
made it worse!

Juan and his brother were playing at a friend's house,
Their Dad came along and said, "It's time to come home,"
But Juan just complained, "Let us stay here and play!"
He hollered and yelled, thinking he'd get his way.

Even though it's hard to understand,
Don't let yourself get way out of hand,
Things are not as bad as they seem,
It's self-control for you and me!

© 1998 Angel Creek Music

Self-Control

Finale from "Light Cavalry" Overture
Suppe'

Well, I look to the left and I look to the right,
And the food that I see is so tempting,
A three-layer cake, mom told me to wait,
But I don't know how long I can.
There's a strawberry pie and a chocolate bar,
And some green jellybeans on the counter,
With my appetite, I'd eat every bite, If it wasn't for self-control.

Well, I go to the store with my mom and my dad,
There's that toy that I want, can I have it?
It's big and it's blue, and it's shiny and new,
And all of my friends have one, too. Well, my father says, "No."
And, "It's time that we go,"

But I know that I can't live without it,
I'd kick and I'd scream, and I'd make a big scene,
If it wasn't for self-control.

Chorus
Self-control when you're wanting to do the
thing that you shouldn't do.
Self-control's what you need for that feeling
that comes over you.
When you're tempted to do it,
And you need a way through it,
If only you have self-control and make it your goal,
You will do what is right in the end.

Well, I look to the left and I look to the right,
On our field trip to the museum,
They tell me, 'Don't touch!" I want to so much,
My hands have a mind of their own.
In class at the school or a library room,
When they tell me I'm supposed to be quiet,
But I want to shout, I'd let it out,
If it wasn't for self-control.
There's a sign over here and a sign over there,
And they all tell me not to do something,
Don't run in the hall, no bouncing the ball,
No diving at all in the pool.
Well, it's hard not to run if I want to have fun,
And the ball doesn't want to stop bouncing,
I'd dive in the pool and break every rule,
If it wasn't for self-control.
Chorus
We need self-control,
Let's make it our goal, self-control,
We need to have self-control,
Let's try to make it our goal,
Self-control, we need some self-control. Self-Control!

© 1998 Angel Creek Music

Crossword Puzzle

Write the correct word in the blank. Then write the word in the puzzle. The words are listed in the box below.

control	refrain	share	help	listen
wait	nicely	count	upset	obey

ACROSS

1. ______________ your temper.
2. Do not get ______________ when things don't go your way.
3. ______________ your toys with others.
4. Talk ______________ to others.

DOWN

1. ______________ to ten when you're angry.
2. ______________ for your turn patiently.
3. ______________ others when you can.
4. ______________ carefully to instructions.
5. ______________ from cookies before dinner.
6. ______________ the rules.

Go Fly a Kite

Have you ever flown a kite? Color the kites blue that have words showing self-control on them.

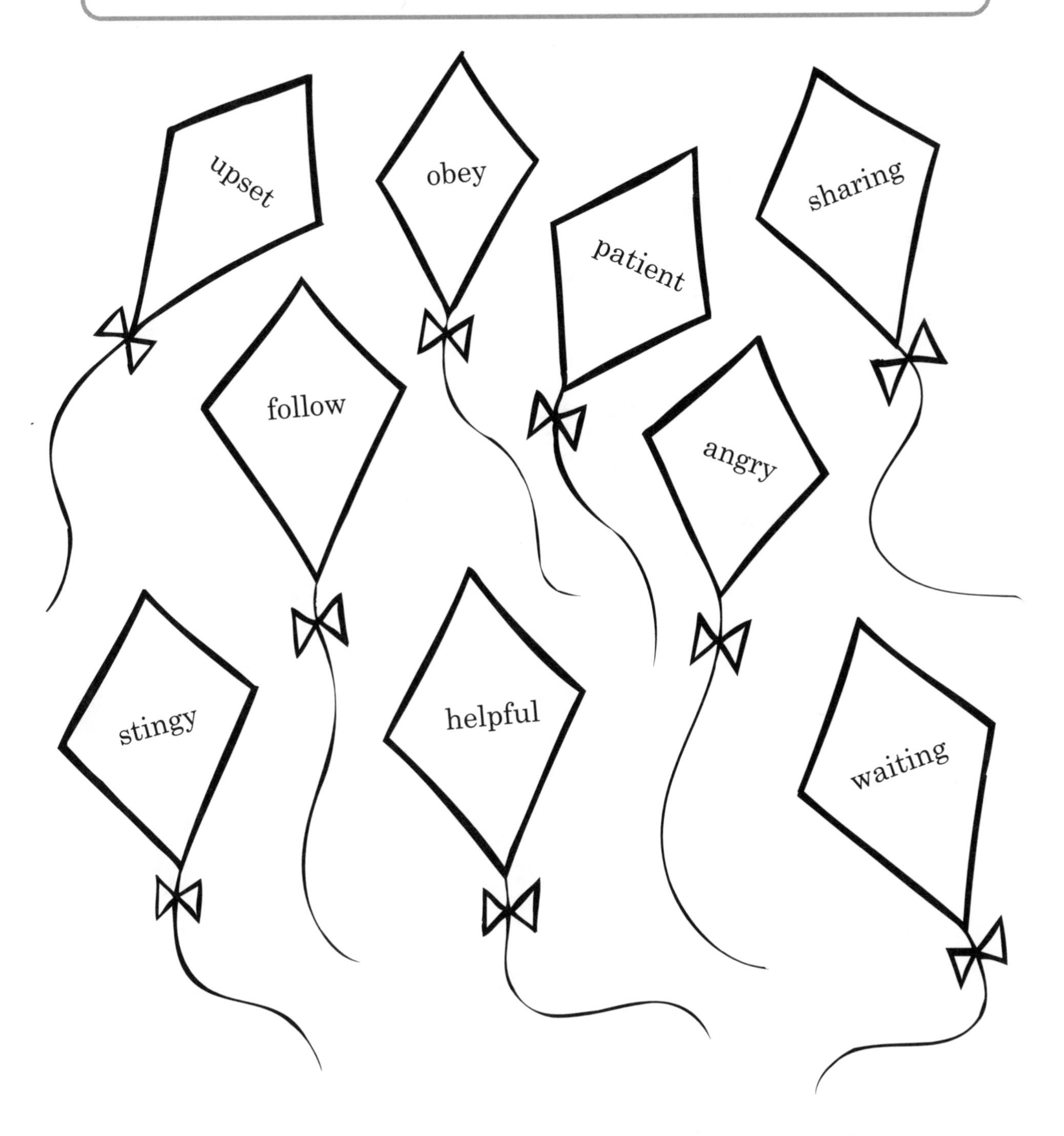

How may blue self-controlled kites do you count? _______
How many kites are not self-controlled and should be grounded?

____

Break the Code

Break the code and discover an important message. To find the answer use the Code Box to fill in the blanks with letters for each number.

CODE BOX																									
1	2	3	4	5	6	7	8	9	10	11	12	13	14	15	16	17	18	19	20	21	22	23	24	25	26
A	B	C	D	E	F	G	H	I	J	K	L	M	N	O	P	Q	R	S	T	U	V	W	X	Y	Z

Self – ___ ___ ___ ___ ___ ___ ___

is bringing my

___ ___ ___ ___ ___ ___ ___ ___,

___ ___ ___ ___ ___,

and

___ ___ ___ ___ ___ ___ ___

under control.

Name three ways that show you have self-control:

1. ______________________________
2. ______________________________
3. ______________________________

True or False

Read each true or false statement. Circle the correct code letter. Match the numbers of the statements to the numbers below the blanks. Fill in the blanks with the circled letter to discover a hidden message.

True	False		Statement
T	M	1.	I am self-controlled when I follow the rules.
P	C	2.	I am self-controlled when I throw a temper.
R	X	3.	I am self-controlled when I don't get upset if things don't go my way.
K	O	4.	I am self-controlled when I take whatever I want without asking.
L	D	5.	I am self-controlled when I do my homework before I watch TV.
E	Y	6.	I am self-controlled when I shout out the answers without raising my hand.
N	Q	7.	I am self-controlled when I wait my turn in line.
B	I	8.	I am self-controlled when I run away from my mom in the grocery store.
U	I	9.	I am self-controlled when I wait for my turn to speak in the conversation.
S	H	10.	I am self-controlled when I take time to read and follow the directions.
G	A	11.	I am self-controlled when I interrupt grown-ups who are talking.

____ ____ ____ ____ ____ ____ ____
2 4 7 1 3 4 5

____ ____ ____ ____   ____ ____ ____ ____ ____ ____ ____ !
6 4 9 3   11 2 1 8 4 7 10

Just a Note

Whenever you lose your temper, it's good to say you're sorry. Think of someone you would like to say you're sorry to and write them a short note.

Dear ________________,

____

____

____

____

____

____

____

____

Thankfulness

thank'ful · ness

Having and showing a genuine attitude of appreciation for any benefits received.

"Every condition and place we are in should be a witness of our thankfulness."
-R. Libbes

TOOLS

Composers

The following composers' melodies were used for the Thankfulness songs.

Luigi Baccherini (BAHK uh REE nee)

Boccherini was born in Italy in 1743 and died in 1805. His family was very musical, and he toured in Vienna and Paris with his cello when he was very young. Even though he wrote hundreds of works, he is best known for one short minuet.

Alexander Borodin (BAWR uh deen)

Borodin was born in Russia in 1833 and died there in 1887. He is the composer of the greatest of all Russian operas, *Prince Igor*. He wrote music while he taught chemistry and conducted scientific research, which he considered his "more serious occupations."

Franz Liszt (list)

Liszt was born in Hungary in 1811 and died in 1886. He was often considered one of the world's greatest pianists, as well as an outstanding composer. Even his worst compositions were liked. He was instructed as a boy by his father, an amateur musician, and gave his first concert at the age of 9 for the prince. The prince was so impressed, he paid for Liszt's education for the next six years. Liszt went to Vienna to study. Today he is considered to be among the greatest pianists of all times.

Franz Schubert (SHOO buhrt)

Schubert is one of the few musicians who was actually born in the musical city of Vienna. He was born in 1797 and died there in 1828 at the age of 31 of typhus. He showed musical talent at a very young age and wrote music all of his life. However, very few were published during his lifetime and he was always poor. He applied twice, without success, for a position for an orchestral conductor. He wrote several operas to earn money, but they were never performed. Today he is considered the world's greatest songwriter.

Peter Tchaikovsky (chy COFF skee)

Tchaikovsky, whose name can also be spelled Tschaikowsky, was born in Russia in 1840 and died there in 1893. His family moved a lot when he was young, so he was very shy. After studying to be a lawyer, he turned to music at the age of 22. He was able to express his emotions through his music, and today he is considered the greatest of all Russian composers. His melodies are among the most beautiful ever written.

Lyrics

Thank You Very Much!

String Quartet in E Major - Menuetto
Luigi Baccherini

Verse 1
Thank you very much, four words you need to know,
Thank you very much, to let your feel-ings show,
A communication of appreciation,
All you say is "thank you very much."

Thank you very much, when someone holds the door,
Thank you very much, if someone gives you more,
It's an attitude, of your gratitude,
Can you say it? "thank you very much."

For all you do,
We say, "thank you!"

Thank you very much, you sure look great today,
Thank you very much, is all you have to say,
It's a demonstration of appreciation,
When you say it, "thank you very much."

For all you do,
We say, "thank you!"

Thank you very much, it's not so hard to say,
Thank you very much, let's say it every-day,
Such a simple saying, now without delaying,
Can you say it? "thank you very much."

Verse 2
Thank you very much, you made my lunch for me,
Thank you very much, you did my laun-da-ry,
A communication of appreciation,
All you say is "thank you very much."

Thank you very much, you took me on that hike,
Thank you very much, you fixed my favorite bike,
It's an attitude, of your gratitude,
Can you say it? "thank you very much."

For all you do,
We say, "thank you!"

Thank you very much, for giving me a lift,
Thank you very much, I love my birthday gift,
It's a demonstration of appreciation,
When you say it, "thank you very much."

For all you do,
We say, "thank you!"

Thank you very much, it's not so hard to say,
Thank you very much, let's say it every-day,
Such a simple saying, now without delaying,
Can you say it? "thank you very much."

Things I Am Thankful For

Polovtsian Dance #17
from Prince Igor
Alexander Borodin

Verse 1
School bell rings,
Now it's time to go out and play,
Cartoons on a Saturday,
All things I am thankful for.
My family camping trips,
Taking rides on a motor boat,
Popcorn and a root beer float,
All things I am thankful for.

Chorus
One day you're feeling sad,
And nothing is going right,
It's really not so bad,
Remember the things you like,
Sit down and close your eyes,
What things are you thankful for?
And now you realize,
You're not sad any more.

Verse 2
Cold ice cream,
At the park on a summer day,
The sun shining on my face,
Some things I am thankful for.
When I can stay up late,
On vacations and holidays,
A swim in the ocean waves,
All things I am thankful for.

Chorus
One day you're feeling sad,
And nothing is going right,
It's really not so bad,
Remember the things you like,

Sit down and close your eyes,
What things are you thankful for?
And now you realize,
You're not sad any more.

Verse 3
Shooting stars,
And the moon on a winter night,
So big and it shines so bright,
The things I am thankful for.
I see the snow that falls,
Like a feather from up above,
It's Christmas I'm dreaming of,
All things I am thankful for.

Ending
Think about the things you are thankful for.
Close your eyes, dream of what you are thankful for.
Don't forget all the things you are thank-ful for.

The Inventor's Song

Sleeping Beauty - Waltz
Peter Tchaikovsky

Chorus
Thank-you, Thomas Edison, for the lights that shine,
Alexander Graham Bell, thank-you for the
telephone line,
And to Orville and Wilbur Wright,
we're so glad your airplane flew!
For these inventions we're grateful to you!

Verse 1
The book that I'm reading,
The Gutenburg press was a printing suc-cess,
And the blue jeans I'm wearing,
I'm grateful to old Levi Strauss.
The car that I ride in,
When climbing on board I will thank Henry Ford,
Rubber tires from Dunlop,
For all these inventions we'll always be thankful.

Chorus
Thank-you, Thomas Edison, for the lights that shine,
Alexander Graham Bell, thank-you for
the telephone line,

And to Orville and Wilbur Wright,
we're so glad your airplane flew!
For these inventions we're grateful to you!

Verse 2
The food that I'm eating,
I love peanut butter, George Washington Carver,
For dinner, my favorite,
Mr. Krafts's macaroni and cheese!
The Earl of Sandwich,
Was John Montagu he invented it, too!
For cheeseburgers and french fries,
For all these inventions we'll always be thankful.

Chorus
Thank-you, Thomas Edison, for the lights that shine,
Alexander Graham Bell, thank-you for
the telephone line,
And to Orville and Wilbur Wright,
we're so glad your airplane flew!
For these inventions we're grateful to you!

For All You Do

Liebestraum #3 - Dream of Love
Franz Liszt

Chorus
For all you do,
I won't forget to thank you,
Thank you for all you do.
Where would I be,
Without you there to help me?
Thank you for all you do.

Chorus
For all you do,
We won't forget to thank you,
Thank you for all you do.
You help us through,
Where would we be without you,
Thank you for all you do.

Verse 1
You helped me tie my shoes,
You find the things I lose,
When "I don't get it!"
You explain,
Take the blame for me,
Lose the game for me,
That's what you do!

Chorus
For all you do,
I won't forget to thank you,
Thank you for all you do.
Where would I be,
Without you there to help me?
Thank you for all you do.

Verse 2
You answer all my "whys",
You give me extra tries,
Good times, bad times,
You are there,
Anywhere with me,
Things you share with me,
That's what you do!

Chorus
For all you do,
We won't forget to thank you,
Thank you for all you do.
You help us through,
Where would we be without you,
Thank you for all you do.

Be Thankful

Quintet in A 4th Movement
Franz Schubert

Verse 1
Be thankful for your best friend,
All the crazy games you play,
For holidays and weekends,
Cartoons on a Saturday,
Be thankful for your dinner,
Barbecuing juicy steaks,
The smell of fresh strawberries,
Or pie that has just been baked.

Chorus
So take a minute, look around you,
Tell me everything you see,
And we will all be thankful,
Thankful we will be,
Let us all be thankful,
Thankful you and me.

Verse 2
Be thankful for your teacher,
Every lesson you will learn,
And for the firefighters,
Who make sure that nothing burns,
Be thankful for the butchers,
All the meat that they will chop,
Be thankful for your doctor,
The nurse and the traffic cop.

Chorus
Just take a minute, look around you,
Tell me everything you see,
And we will all be thankful,
Thankful we will be,
Let us all be thankful,
Thankful you and me.

Verse 3
Be thankful for the sunshine,
For the flowers and the trees,
For every living creature,
The whale to the tiny flea,
Be thankful for the ocean,
Building castles in the sand,
For summertime and rainbows,
And trips to a distant land.

Chorus
So take a minute, look around you,
Tell me everything you see,
And we will all be thankful,
Thankful we will be,
Let us all be thankful,
Thankful you and me.

Code Busters

Each symbol represents a word. Look them over carefully and fill in the blank with the word that matches each symbol.

Thankfulness is ________________ ▲

and ________________ ■ a

________________ ★ ________________ ●

of ________________ ❤ for any

________________ ◆ received.

- ❤ appreciation
- ● attitude
- ◆ benefits
- ★ genuine
- ▲ having
- ■ showing

Thank You, Mr. Webster

Noah Webster was born in 1758 before the Revolutionary War. He spent ten years studying the English language and how it was connected to other languages.

In 1828 his dictionary was published. It has been the standard dictionary of the English language since that time. Webster felt a need for providing his countrymen with the simplest form of pronunciation and spelling of the English language. It took almost 18 years of hard work to bring us our first dictionary.

We thank you, Mr. Webster!

Let's define THANKFULNESS!

Get our your dictionary and look up the words below.
Write out the definition on the lines.

THANK: ______________________________

____

____

THANKFUL: ______________________________

____

____

Now, you write your own definition of **THANKFULNESS:** __________

____

____

Break the code below to find two of the most important words in any language.

□ ⌜ ⌝ ⌞ ⊓

___ ___ ___ ___ ___

⊔ ⊐ ⊏

___ ___ ___

W	Y	N
O	T	U
A	K	H

Almost the Same

A synonym is a word that has the same or almost the same meaning as another word. Find two important words below by breaking the code. Match the numbers in the puzzle with the letters in the Code Box. Write the correct letter in the box.

CODE BOX

1	2	3	4	5	6	7	8	9	10	11	12	13	14	15	16	17	18	19	20	21	22	23	24	25	26
A	B	C	D	E	F	G	H	I	J	K	L	M	N	O	P	Q	R	S	T	U	V	W	X	Y	Z

				7					
				18					
				1					
				20					
1	16	16	18	5	3	9	1	20	5
				6					
				21					
				12					

Write the synonyms here.

1. ______________________________
2. ______________________________

Who are you going to show appreciation to today?

Write their name here: ____________________

What is one thing you are grateful for today?

Write it here: ____________________________

Jot-a-Note

Can you think of somone that you are thankful for? (Hint – hint!! – your mother, dad, brother, sister, grandparent, a friend, a neighbor, a teacher)

Write them a note and tell them today! Make a copy of the letter and give or send it to them right away! It will make them feel good, and you, too!

Can you think of any others that you are thankful for?

- ☐ ______________________ ☐ ______________________
- ☐ ______________________ ☐ ______________________
- ☐ ______________________ ☐ ______________________

Try to write another letter tomorrow and the next day until all the names are checked off your list. Happy writing!

Word Search

All of the people listed below are people to be thankful for. Find and circle all of the people in the puzzle below. The first one is circled for you.

L	K	E	A	X	M	B	Z	M	O	T	H	E	R
B	T	G	R	A	N	D	P	A	R	E	N	T	S
A	A	E	W	N	E	I	G	H	B	O	R	N	F
B	D	R	A	U	J	G	P	Y	N	B	U	U	G
Y	S	U	Y	C	L	H	L	E	O	I	F	R	Y
S	R	N	K	Y	H	P	I	L	R	R	A	S	P
I	L	C	F	I	R	E	F	I	G	H	T	E	R
T	F	L	Z	L	T	A	R	F	E	A	H	G	A
T	S	E	P	O	L	I	C	E	A	V	E	O	D
E	O	I	N	G	U	Y	S	G	T	E	R	T	O
R	P	D	S	J	C	C	O	U	S	I	N	S	C
Z	A	U	N	T	O	H	A	A	T	Q	H	F	T
A	U	T	Y	R	E	I	R	R	U	U	A	A	O
B	R	O	T	H	E	R	E	D	N	E	S	R	R

1. ~~AUNT~~
2. BABYSITTER
3. BROTHER
4. COUSINS
5. DOCTOR
6. FATHER
7. FIREFIGHTER
8. GRANDPARENTS
9. LIFEGUARD
10. MOTHER
11. NEIGHBOR
12. NURSE
13. POLICE
14. SISTER
15. TEACHER
16. UNCLE

Truthfulness

truth'· ful · ness

Making sure that my words and actions are accurate, genuine, and factual so that I am a reliable messenger.

"Truth is generally the best vindication against slander."

-Abraham Lincoln

Composers

The following composers' melodies were used for the Truthfulness songs.

Leonard Gautier

(go´-tee-a)

No historical background information was found on Gautier, but his musical contribution is significant. Although he may be an obscure composer, his melodies are well-known.

Modest Mussorgsky

(ma-zorg´-ski)

Modest Petrovich Mussorgsky was born in the Ukraine of Russia on March 28, 1839. He died on his birthday, March 28, in St. Petersburg in 1881. He is considered one of the most important Russian composers and is called the "father" of the whole modern movement there. He was first taught piano by his mother. He started composing his own music before he turned 20 years old.

Wolfgang Amadeus Mozart

(moats'-art)

Wolfgang Amadeus' real name was Johannes Chrysostomus Wolfgangus Theophilus Mozart. He was born in Salzburg, Austria, on January 27, 1756, and died in Vienna on December 5, 1791, at the young age of 35. He began to play the piano at the age of 3. When he was 5, he could play several instruments and wrote his first music. At 7 he went on his first musical tour with his family. He is considered by some, the greatest musical genius of all time.

Johann Strauss, Jr.

(strous)

Strauss was born in Vienna on October 25, 1825, and died there on June 3, 1899. He was the son of another famous Strauss (Johann Sr.) who was considered the "father" of the waltz. Johann Jr. wrote his first waltz at the age of 6 and conducted a very successful orchestral concert when only 19 years old. He was known as the "Waltz King."

A. G. Villoldo

(vee-yole´-doe)

Angel Gregorio Villoldo was born in 1860 and died in 1919. Many people consider him the "Father of the Tango."

Lyrics

Let Your Yes Be Yes

Pictures At An Exhibition
The Gate of Kiev
Modest Mussorgsky

Let your yes be yes
And let your no be no
Then your words will show
You are true and trustworthy
In everything you do and
all you say everyday
You can show the world a
bright
and a new way!

When you talk about others
Keep the truth intact,
Don't forget the facts.
Tell the truth in your stories
Always tell the truth and
keep the message clear
Say the words you only hear
with your two ears

Let your yes be yes
And let your no be no
Speak words pure as gold

Speak the truth everyday!
Show the way!

Fibber Fred

The Secret
Leonard Gautier

Here's a tale, hear a tale, of
a boy named
Fibber Fred who never
Told the truth in all
the many things he said
and,
Like a snowball that rolls
down a hillside,
Lies get bigger as they roll
and roll until they roll out of
control
O, Fred told a lie to his
teacher while at school
And when she called on the
phone to his home,
Fred answered and he said
that he was alone
But his mom heard the
phone ring and she asked
him
Who was calling, so Fred
fibbed!

Oh, he lied one time, and
then once again.
All his lies were getting him
confused
And that is why his head
began to ache!
It would surely break!
Telling lies is so confusing
in the end.

Fibber Fred finally said that
his teacher had just called
Upon the phone to his home
to tell his mother he had lied
That day at school, broke
the rules, telling lies
Is not a good thing for the
boys
and girls to do,
Their words must say what's
true, so Fred, now he said,
He was wrong to tell a lie,
and from now on,
He would say what was true
and not a fib and so he
Did change his ways and
today
he is known
To all the children as the
honest,
truthful Fred.

O his lie grew big as he told
his fib,
Suddenly his head began to
spin
And that is why his head
began to ache.
Would it surely break?
Telling lies is so confusing,
It is really not amusing in
the end!

The Truthful Toad

Piano Concerto No. 20
Romance
Wolfgang Amadeus Mozart

I'd rather tell the truth than
tell a lie,
I'm the truthful toad, I can-
not deny it,
As you see, I'm just a real
honest guy,
I'm the Truthful Toad of
Toadville.

He'd rather tell the truth
than tell a lie,
He is the truthful toad, we
cannot deny it,
As you see, he is just a real
honest guy,
He is the Truthful Toad of
Toadville.

Soon you'll discover, I'm like
no other,
I'm always truthful, just ask
my mother!
(Or my sister or my brother
or my father!)
I'd rather tell the truth than
tell a lie,
I'm the Truthful Toad of
Toadville.

One day the royal princess
came to town,
Saw the truthful toad just
hopping around,
She said, "If I kiss you,
will you turn into a prince,
You're the Truthful Toad of
Toadville."

Oh, princess I could never
tell a lie,
I'm the truthful toad, I can-
not deny it,
As you see, what I am is
what I'll always be,
I'm the Truthful Toad of
Toadville.

So I've discovered, you're
like no other,
Come to the castle, to meet
my father!
My mother and my ten
brothers!
Now, over to the castle we'll
go,
You'll be the Royal Toad forever!

She has discovered, he's
like no other,
Went to the castle,
to meet her father!
Then, over to the castle
they did go,
He'll be the
Royal Toad forever!!

Tell the Truth

On the Beautiful Blue
Danube Waltz
Johann Strauss, Jr.

When people ask why, just
tell the truth,
When people ask how, just
tell the truth,
When people ask where,
just tell the truth,
When people ask who, just
tell the truth,
When people ask when, just
tell the truth,
When people ask what, just
tell the truth,
When people ask questions
of you,
You must always, always tell
the truth.

Little Billy broke his big
brother's bike,
Yes he smashed it all to
pieces,
Billy told a lie, said "it was-
n't me,"
Now he's in big trouble
'cause he didn't
tell the truth.

Billy had a friend, Suzy was
her name,
She told tales, made up stories,
Now no one believes any-
thing she says,
This could never happen if
she'd only told the truth.

So learn to tell the truth,
It's the only thing to do,
If you learn to tell the truth,
You can always be sure that
people will trust you.

Soon as dinner's done,
Debbie's out the door,
Father warned her, "Do your
homework!"
Debbie told a lie, said, "I finished it."
Now she's in big trouble
'cause she didn't
tell the truth.

Tommy took something, and
it wasn't his,
When they asked, he said, "I
didn't,"
Now he can't go out with the
other kids,
This would never have hap-
pened if he'd
only told the truth.

So learn to tell the truth,
It's the only thing to do,
If you learn to tell the truth,
You can always be sure that
people
will trust, people will trust
you.

The Wallet

El Choclo
A. G. Villoldo

Little Billy was walking
down the street
And on the sidewalk there
was something by his
feet
He picked it up, it was a wallet
full of money
And little Billy's little tummy
felt so funny

He got excited 'bout the
things
that he could buy
Now he could buy himself a
brand new shiny bike
Then Billy saw there was a
number in the wallet
So he ran home and dialed it
on the phone.

It wasn't easy for him to
make the call
A man named Richard Hall
Said he had lost his wallet
The fact that Billy was honest
made him happy.
So he thanked him time and
time and time again.

He felt so lucky that Billy
found his money
It wasn't very funny
When he couldn't find it.
He knew he'd be wrong if he
kept the wallet
So Billy called because
it was the thing to do!

To show Billy his great
appreciation
Outside the window there
was a present
Before his eyes what a wonderful surprise
It was a brand new shiny
bike.

So if you find a wallet full of
money
And your tummy starts
to feeling kind of funny
Just remember the story
about Billy
You will have a happy feeling in the end.

Word Search

Find and circle all of the words in the puzzle below. The words are listed below the puzzle. The first one has been circled for you.

L	R	U	T	B	C	A	P	P	R	O	V	A	L
M	H	R	E	P	R	E	S	E	N	T	S	P	A
N	O	V	E	C	A	U	O	R	Y	S	K	V	R
M	N	D	M	L	N	T	I	L	I	D	C	W	O
O	E	I	J	F	I	A	E	N	P	J	O	U	M
P	S	S	M	G	F	A	C	T	S	K	L	P	L
R	T	P	S	L	T	E	B	A	H	E	A	R	T
T	A	O	M	E	R	G	C	L	R	B	E	I	E
C	D	S	G	E	N	U	I	N	E	E	C	G	L
U	F	I	N	T	E	G	R	I	T	Y	I	H	L
D	G	T	F	C	H	R	E	B	H	F	T	T	I
N	L	I	S	N	K	N	A	R	F	O	S	D	N
O	M	O	G	X	T	R	U	T	H	F	U	L	G
C	A	N	D	O	R	A	R	L	R	M	J	S	B

√ 1. APPROVAL
2. CANDOR
3. CONDUCT
4. DISPOSITION
5. FACTS
6. FAIR
7. FRANK
8. GENUINE
9. HEART
10. HONEST
11. INTEGRITY
12. JUSTICE
13. MESSENGER
14. MORAL
15. RELIABLE
16. REPRESENT
17. SINCERE
18. TELLING
19. TRUTHFUL
20. UPRIGHT

The Hidden Word

Color each space marked with a letter in the puzzle below. Then write the word in the blank.

Bonus Question

Why is it important that I tell the truth?

Go for the Goal

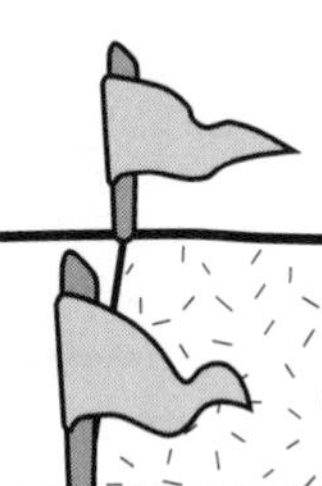

Good Work!
Real winners tell the truth!

You admitted you didn't touch first base, causing your team to lose the game. *Truth.* Move ahead 1 space.

You said the pencil was yours but you'd just found it under your friend's desk. *Lie.* Move back 2 spaces.

You told your mom you have a book report due Monday and weren't allowed to skate with friends. *Truth.* Go ahead 2 spaces.

You told your teacher that your dog ate your homework. *Lie.* Go back to start.

Using dice or a spinner, move your marker around the track.
See how telling the truth may be hard, but helps you reach the goal.

You said you brushed your teeth but you just rinsed with mouth-wash. *Lie.* Move back 1 space.

You told your mom you practiced the piano only 30 minutes instead of 1 hour. *Truth.* Move ahead 1 space.

You blamed your sister for the broken lamp. *Lie.* Lose one turn.

You admitted to your neighbor you broke his window. *Truth.* Take another turn.

Find the Way

Help Fibber Fred find the way to truthfulness. Go through the maze and circle each word that has to do with being truthful. If you circle all the correct words, you will find your way through to truthfulness.

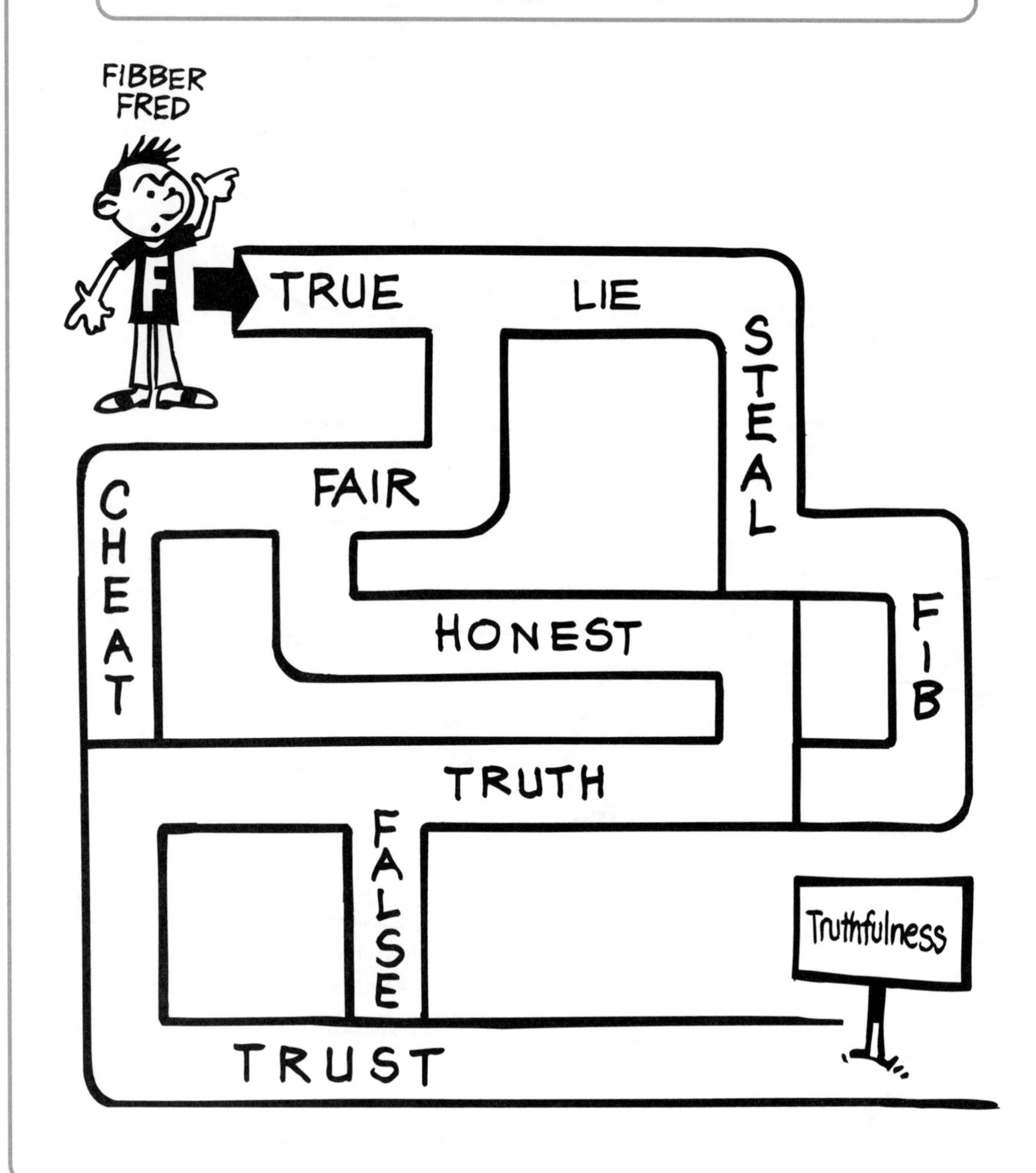

Pledge

I have completed all of the activities
on the character quality:

Attentiveness.

I am learning that attentiveness is being
carefully and sensibly aware of the feelings,
words and needs of others.
I will always try to show attentiveness
in my life everyday.

As of this date

Your name

Pledge

I have completed all of the activities
on the character quality:

Contentment.

I am learning that contentment
is being at peace with who I am
and what I have. I will always
try to show contentment
in my life every day.

As of this date

Your name

Pledge

I have completed all of the activities
on the character quality:

Dependability.

I am learning that dependability
is capable of being relied on or trusted in with
full confidence regardless of circumstances.
I will always try to show
dependability in my life every day.

____________________ As of this date

____________________ Your name

Pledge

I have completed all of the activities
on the character quality:

Goodness.

I am learning that goodness is being
well-behaved, mannerly, and kind, and
doing what is right and proper.
I will always try to show goodness
in my life every day.

____________________ As of this date

____________________ Your name

Pledge

I have completed all of the activities

on the character quality:

Kindness.

I am learning that kindness is

an act of love that adds to the

true happiness of others.

I will always try to show acts of

kindness in my life every day.

____________________ ____________________

As of this date Your name

Pledge

I have completed all of the activities

on the character quality:

Obedience.

I am learning that obedience is responding

to the wishes or commands of those in authority

who care for me.

I will always try to show obedience

in my life every day.

____________________ ____________________

As of this date Your name

Pledge

I have completed all of the activities
on the character quality:

Patience.

I am learning that patience is calmly
overcoming and enduring
troubles, delays, and problems
without complaining. I will always try
to show patience in my life every day.

____________________ ____________________

As of this date Your name

Pledge

I have completed all of the activities
on the character quality:

Perseverance.

I am learning that perseverance is not giving up,
but staying with any task, job,
or purpose until it is completed.
I will always try to show perseverance
in my life every day.

____________________ ____________________

As of this date Your name

Pledge

I have completed all of the activities
on the character quality:

Respect.

I am learning that respect is showing courteous
consideration, honor, and appreciation for others,
their property, and the environment
around me. I will always try to
show respect in my life every day.

As of this date ____________ Your name ____________

Pledge

I have completed all of the activities
on the character quality:

Self-Control.

I am learning that self-control
is bringing my thoughts, words,
and actions under control.
I will always try to practice
self-control in my life every day.

As of this date ____________ Your name ____________

Pledge

I have completed all of the activities
on the character quality:

Thankfulness.

I am learning that thankfulness is having and
showing a genuine attitude of appreciation
for any benefits received.
I will always try to show
thankfulness in my life every day.

______________________ ______________________
As of this date Your name

Pledge

I have completed all of the activities
on the character quality:

Truthfulness.

I am learning that truthfulness is making sure
that my words and actions are accurate, genuine,
and factual so that I may be a reliable messenger.
I will always try to be truthful
in my life every day.

______________________ ______________________
As of this date Your name

Answer Key

Answers are for the less obvious actvities.

Word Search (p. 8)

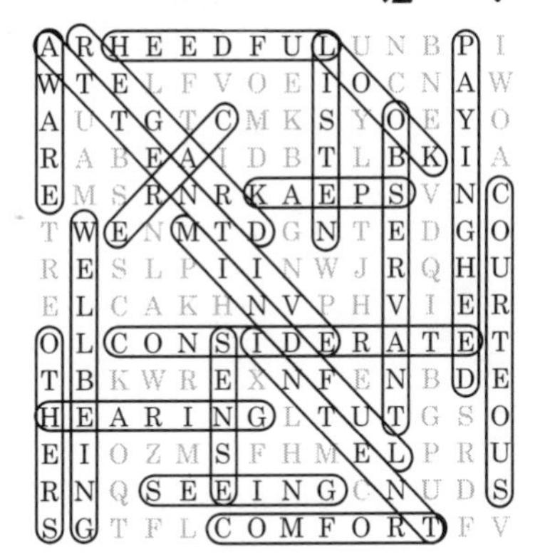

Secret Message (p. 9)

Answer: Pay Attention

Picnic Path (p. 10)

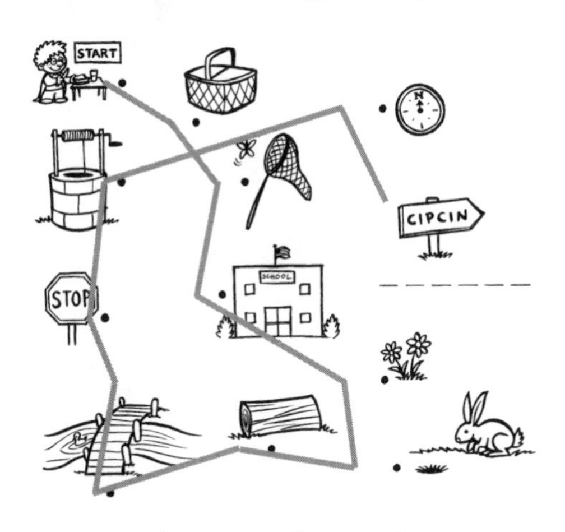

If I Listen (p. 11)

4, 1, 6, 5, 2, 3

Pay Attention (p. 12)

1	*5*
2	*6*
4	*3*

Find the Secret (p. 16)

HAT	*SUN*
TENT	*FISH*
DOOR	*WAGON*

HE IS SATISFIED WITH WHAT HE HAS.

Word Search (p. 17)

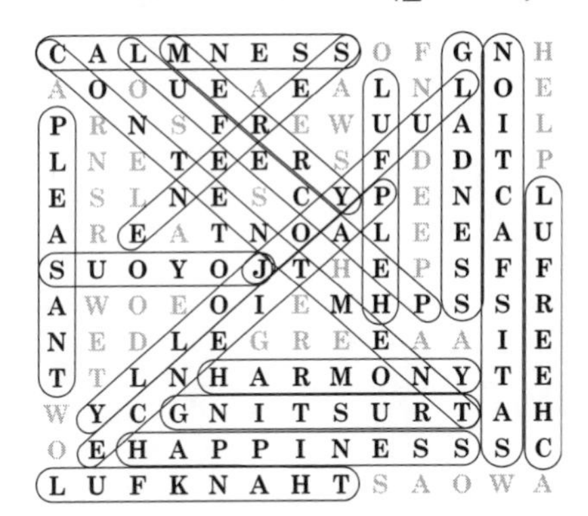

A Secret Message (p. 18)

BE CONTENT.

Break the Code (p. 19)

Contentment is BEING at PEACE with WHO YOU ARE and WHAT YOU HAVE.

Crossword Puzzle (p. 20)

		2					3				
1 H	A	P	P	Y			J				
		E		5			O				
	4 H	A	R	M	O	N	Y				
		C		E							
6 C	H	E	E	R	F	U	L				
		F		R				7			
		U	9	Y	10			G			
8 H	E	L	P		I			R			
			L		N			A			
		11	E	N	V	Y		T			
			A		I			E			
12 D	I	S	S	A	T	I	S	F	I	E	D
			E		E			U			
			D		S			L			

Answer Key

Can You Depend on It? (p. 24)

YES | NO

Word Search (p. 25)

T A E V E I L E B A I E L N
O T R U T H A A O R B B T E
Y T U D R O A E L B A T S A
C A S E U N D F M A N O A T
O D L E T E A R I W O W F N
N Y E Y E S I M O R P J D E
F E D P U T U V E W M E A T
I L P A E C A R E F U L E S
D B I D E N O X T R O S T I
E A G O L T D Y D I L O S S
N I A E E Y S L L O Y A L N
C L R R M F A I T H F U L O
E E T N E M T I M M O C L C
D R E T N A T S N O C Z Q A

Crossword Puzzle (p. 26)

Missing Letters (p. 27)

RELIABLE

Alphabet Code (p. 28)

CAPABLE
RELIED
TRUSTED
CONFIDENCE
CIRCUMSTANCES

Code Busters (p. 32)

ONE GOOD DEED BRINGS FORTH ANOTHER.

Break the Code (p. 33)

*Goodness is **BEING WELL-BEHAVED, MANNERLY,** and **KIND**; doing what is **RIGHT** and **PROPER**.*

Crossword Puzzle (p. 34)

Goodness Meal (p. 35)

happy hamburger
thoughtful tamales
praises punch
kindness cake
compliment cookies
courteous custard
polite pudding
mannerly muffins

Answer Key

Maze for the Answer (p. 36)

I Q F P Y O E R D E K Y E Y A O
P E T U M S
J O O Z L E I P U
Z F T T D
I U C W A O J U A R G F N
U R Y K L E
T K F R S T L G E T N H D J H
K
D A O M O N G B E V B C Y X P Z P L A

"IF YOU WOULD KEEP YOUNG AND HAPPY, BE GOOD!"

Use the Right Bait (p. 40)

Word Search (p. 41)

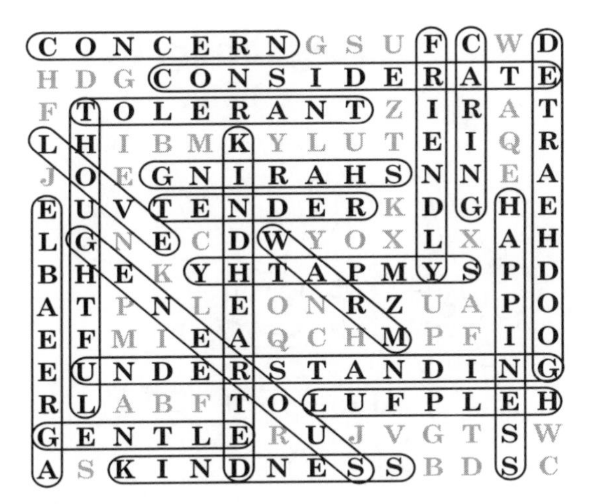

Word Puzzle (p. 42)

k	i	n	d	n	s
n	i	c	e	h	o
s	h	a	r	e	h
d	o	r	i	l	e
t	a	e	s	p	a
o	h	a	p	p	y

1. Always be ***kind***.
2. ***Share*** your toys.
3. Be ***nice*** to others.
4. ***Care*** for those in need.
5. When you are kind you make others ***happy***.
6. When you ***help*** others you are showing kindness.

Words of Kindness (p. 43)

Kind	*Kind*
Unkind	*Kind*
Unkind	*Unkind*

Show Kindness (p. 44)

Be kind to animals.

Word Search (p. 48)

Y	D	B	H	K	R	S	F	O	L	L	O	W	G	X	F	Z
A	I	N	S	T	R	U	C	T	I	O	N	S	H	M	U	Y
G	R	E	I	O	J	B	L	J	P	R	A	A	D	R	L	I
C	E	F	L	R	Q	M	N	E	Q	T	E	R	N	O	F	B
A	C	E	N	D	E	I	R	L	S	N	H	S	E	F	I	Y
U	T	L	M	E	O	S	Y	E	B	O	Q	R	P	R	L	M
T	I	T	P	R	M	S	L	H	K	C	G	A	E	E	L	C
H	O	Q	E	S	G	I	C	T	I	J	T	S	D	P	C	E
O	N	R	V	N	U	O	B	E	D	I	E	N	C	E	D	T
R	S	W	Y	A	D	N	R	E	S	P	O	N	D	N	P	X
I	C	O	M	P	L	I	A	N	T	E	B	V	F	S	J	O
T	X	A	G	R	E	E	A	B	L	E	U	T	U	L	V	C
Y	B	F	S	D	Z	S	U	R	R	E	N	D	E	R	W	K

Answer Key

Find the Words (p. 49)

BOAT
FLOWERS
BUTTERFLY
PEN
OBEY YOUR PARENTS

Mystery Message (p. 50)

You feel good inside.

Code Buster (p. 51)

OBEDIENCE SHOULD BE

PROMPT AND CHEERFUL!

Find the Letter (p. 52)

I should have a ***GOOD ATTITUDE***

when I am asked to do something.

Patience Puzzler (p. 56)

1. ***close***	6. ***clear***
2. ***little***	7. ***begin***
3. ***finish***	8. ***laugh***
4. ***out***	9. ***down***
5. ***come***	10. ***top***

PATIENCE WITHOUT COMPLAINT

Patience Maze (p. 57)

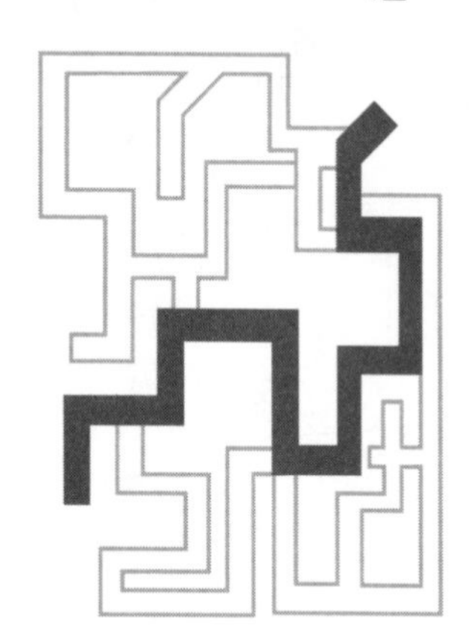

Crossword Puzzle (p. 58)

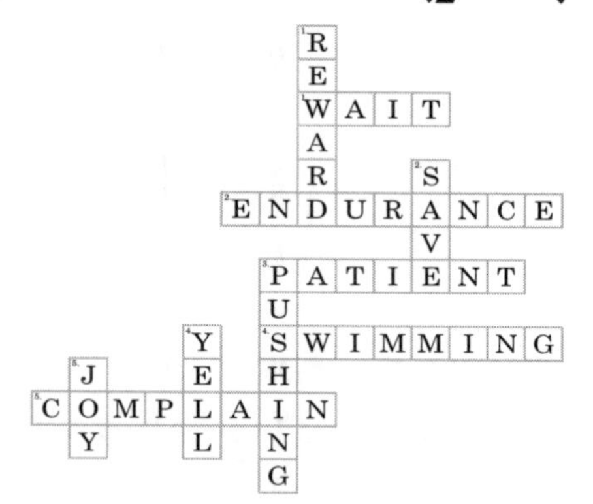

Fishing for Patience (p. 59)

content
calmness
serene
restraint
enduring
waiting
composure
peaceful

Number Message (p. 64)

Answer: Good inside

An Amazing Job (p. 65)

Answer Key

Puzzle Message (p. 66)

Answer: Don't give up!

Try, Try Again (p. 68)

Won't Quit!

Number Message (p. 72)

EAR
BARN
MOON
HOUSE
TOP
YARN

Honor Your Parents

Who Is Showing Respect? (p. 73)

Maze for the Answer (p. 74)

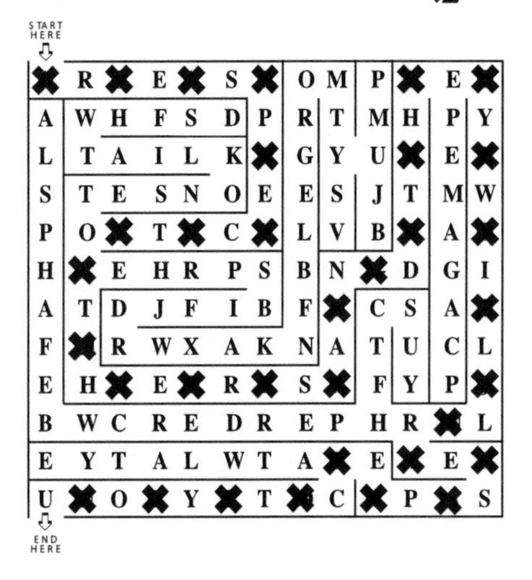

Respect others and they will respect you.

Word Search (p. 75)

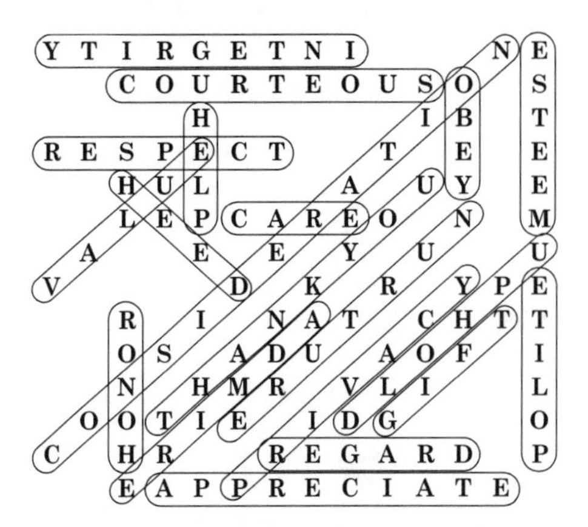

Crossword Puzzle (p. 80)

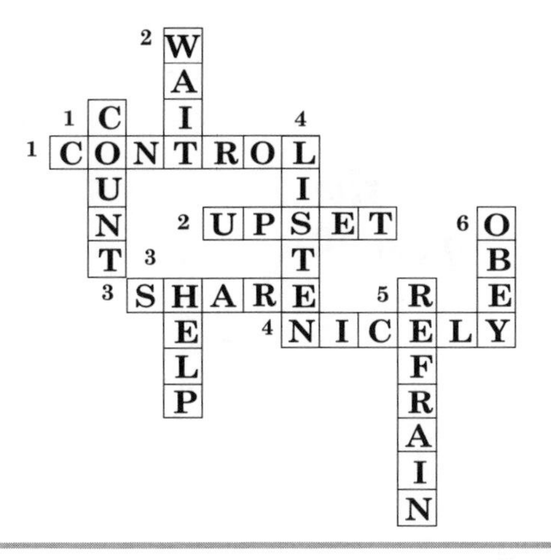

Answer Key

Go Fly a Kite (p. 81)

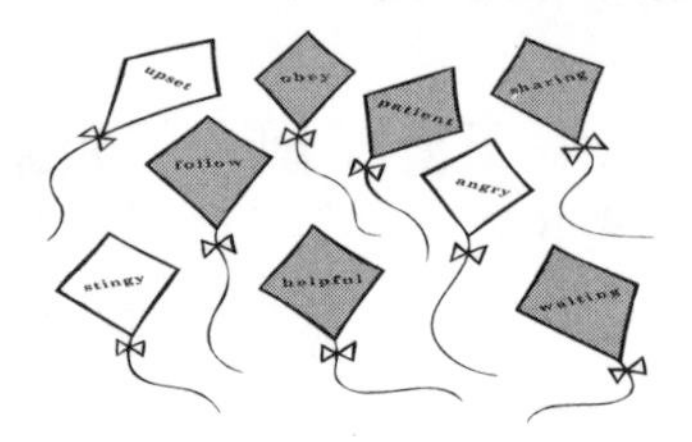

6 blue kites and 3 grounded kites

Break the Code (p. 82)

Self-control is bringing my thoughts, words, and actions under control.

True or False (p. 83)

1. T	4. O	7. N	10. S
2. C	5. L	8. I	11. A
3. R	6. Y	9. U	

CONTROL YOUR ACTIONS!

Code Busters (p. 88)

Thankfulness is HAVING and SHOWING a GENUINE ATTITUDE of APPRECIATION for any BENEFITS received.

Thank You, Mr. Webster (p. 89)

T H A N K

Y O U

Almost the Same (p. 90)

1. GRATEFUL
2. APPRECIATE

Word Search (p. 92)

L	K	E	A	X	M	B	Z	M	O	T	H	E	R
B	T	G	R	A	N	D	P	A	R	E	N	T	S
A	A	E	W	N	E	I	G	H	B	O	R	N	F
B	D	R	A	U	J	G	P	Y	N	B	U	U	G
Y	S	U	Y	C	L	H	L	E	O	I	F	R	Y
S	R	N	K	Y	H	P	I	L	R	R	A	S	P
I	L	C	F	I	R	E	F	I	G	H	T	E	R
T	F	L	Z	L	T	A	R	F	E	A	H	G	A
T	S	E	P	O	L	I	C	E	A	V	E	O	D
E	O	I	N	G	U	Y	S	G	T	E	R	T	O
R	P	D	S	J	C	C	O	U	S	I	N	S	C
Z	A	U	N	T	O	H	A	A	T	Q	H	F	T
A	U	T	Y	R	E	I	R	R	U	U	A	A	O
B	R	O	T	H	E	R	E	D	N	E	S	R	R

Word Search (p. 96)

L	R	U	T	B	C	A	P	P	R	O	V	A	L
M	H	R	E	P	R	E	S	E	N	T	S	P	A
N	O	V	E	C	A	U	O	R	Y	S	K	V	R
M	N	D	Y	L	N	T	I	L	I	D	C	W	O
O	E	I	J	F	I	A	E	N	P	J	O	U	M
P	S	S	M	G	F	A	C	T	S	K	L	P	L
R	T	P	S	L	T	E	B	A	H	E	A	R	T
T	A	O	M	E	R	G	C	L	R	B	E	I	E
C	D	S	G	E	N	U	I	N	E	E	C	G	L
U	F	I	N	T	E	G	R	I	T	Y	I	H	L
D	G	T	F	C	H	R	E	B	H	F	T	T	I
N	L	I	S	N	K	N	A	R	F	O	S	D	N
O	M	O	G	X	T	R	U	T	H	F	U	L	G
C	A	N	D	O	R	A	R	L	R	M	J	S	B

The Hidden Word (p. 97)

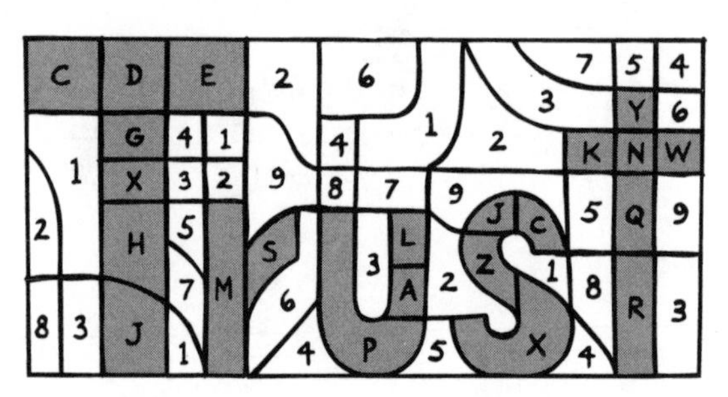

Answer: If I tell the truth, people will ***trust*** *me.*